How t
of Brilliant Leadership in the
New Aged Care Era

RESIDENTIAL
AGED CARE
TRANSFORMED

ALLISON PATCHETT

The information provided in this book will give anyone working within aged care all the tools for the job. Understanding your people is not an easy task, but this book supplies practical steps for supporting staff in providing excellent care within this complex healthcare setting.

I think all the 'Julies' out there will benefit from the information provided.

– Faye Powell, Nurse Manager

A fabulous resource and a must read for every residential aged care facility manager. This book gets to the core of great leadership in the residential aged care setting without unnecessary overcomplication. It will change how you do what you do.

– Jane Daley, General Manager Quality and Clinical Governance

This book makes a very meaningful contribution to the transformation of management and leadership in the new aged care environment. Each chapter of the book has strong messages with relevant and appropriate exercises to help initiate the leadership journey. It provides practically grounded templates for refreshing aged care leadership skills by implementing simple and proven strategies.

– Nickie Arthur, Client Services Manager

For Isobel and Tom, Naomi and Michael:
tremendously loving, funny and generous
grandparents who have shown their grandchildren that
love is without boundaries, and that life is precious
and to be lived to its fullest extent.

Disclaimer

Contents

Introduction

On 11 March 2020, the World Health Organization declared COVID-19 a pandemic. Within a few weeks, residential aged care began to take on a different way of operating as things quickly escalated. Since March 2020, 221 Australian residential aged care homes have experienced COVID-19 outbreaks among residents and staff.[1] Twenty homes have had more than 40 COVID-19-positive residents and 58 homes have had more than two deaths each.

Every now and then, we come across something that makes a connection for us. It can capture complex situations in a single act or phrase – and it sticks with us. COVID-19 in residential aged care was that moment of connection. It forced us to consider normal modes of operation and what the consequences were, depending on what actions were taken or not taken. At the same time as COVID-19 was wreaking havoc, we had a Royal Commission into the state of Australia's aged care system, which revealed shocking defects. This Royal Commission resulted in massive legislative changes – some already in place, and some emerging – designed to transform the aged care sector from top to bottom. It's big. It's a mammoth change to business as usual. I wrote this book to address these changes, and the fundamental flaws that have been discovered.

The additional knowledge required to cope with COVID-19 felt small at first, then slowly, like boiling a frog, the impact grew within a very short time span. If you are ever inclined to test this metaphor, you can just place a frog in a pan of hot water – it will jump out. However, if you place a frog in a pan of cold water and put the pan on the heat, the frog will stay inside – and boil. The frog won't realise the temperature is rising. This is exactly how it felt in residential aged care during the early days of COVID-19.

If you're a residential aged care manager already in the job, or perhaps new to the position of managing such a complex environment, this book is for you.

I wrote this book for Julie, a young clinical manager who was asked to step up into a manager position of an aged care home. Things were a little hairy at the time, and the organisation needed someone that they thought they could rely on. Julie was (and is) competent. She has always been focused on providing a great resident experience, quality care and services. Yet, when she stepped up to be a manager, the narrative around her role changed. The things that she was asked to report on and do were things that didn't pertain to the role as she saw it. 'How much money are we getting a day? How much is staffing costing us? How many full beds do we have? What's our messaging out there?' These mixed messages confused her and made her question herself and her ability to meet expectations.

This book is for all the Julies out there – those who really need a helping hand despite not doing the wrong thing. They have the right emphasis, but they need to understand the world that they're working in.

I often hear that new managers and people working in residential aged care hate change. My message in this book is that change is ever-present. Don't fight it – learn to embrace it and use its power to achieve better results in staff management, clinical management and lifestyle results for your residents. There's a belief among registered nurses that if you work in or manage a residential aged care home you've taken an easy option. Nothing could be further than the truth.

If you're like Julie, you have a demanding role that has suddenly become a whole lot more difficult as change flushes through the system. Managing your people will feel like it consumes you, and from time to time, in reality, it will.

In this book, I will take you through a summary of the legislative changes and how they affect you. You'll learn how to lead and manage during this time of change and beyond, while building the confidence and competence of your staff (and your own confidence in leading them).

You'll also learn about:

· the differences between information and communication, and where to use each effectively

· how to recruit for attitude and discover new ways to recruit

· how to become a risk ninja – to know what risk is, and how to use it both in restrictive and enabling ways, whichever is most appropriate

· how to find the leader within yourself.

I have worked in health for over 40 years – in hospitals, government, community care and residential aged care. I have always been interested in creating a servant leadership approach – where the primary goal of the leader is to serve. I'm fascinated in how to get the best out of our people by leading coaching and mentoring them, and giving great customer service. These aspects are often spoken about, yet inconsistently followed through. Sometimes I do encounter servant leaders, but when that person leaves the home they take the positive change with them. This is usually because the servant leadership approach isn't embedded in the fabric of what people do each day.

My professional life's mission is to assist people in realising their potential and the power of giving a great consumer experience. Today, I work as a leadership coach in all aspects of healthcare: as a board member, chair of a board quality committee and a nurse adviser in aged care.

I assist people who are searching for a better way to lead and manage. They are smart people who have great ideas, but need guidance to put structure to their thoughts and build confidence to execute the things they are passionate about.

Most managers in residential aged care I work with want to do their best. They care about their employees and their residents. If you're reading this book, I have no doubt you fall into this category. However, aged care is a complex and demanding work environment. I am committed to assisting managers like you to develop into their best selves.

Certain people have the mark of a great leader, or even a winner. As children, they may be those who choose the games that everyone else plays. Those children grow into adults who appear to be born leaders. In an organisation, they may be the natural leader who is destined to succeed. They command respect. In Shakespeare's play *Henry V*, he called these leaders 'the makers of manners'. Other people follow these people who establish themselves in how they act every day. These people don't rely on hindsight to deliver their best selves as leader and manager. If this is you, great! You already have a strong foundation to build on. If not, don't fear. You don't have to be born a maker of manners; it is a talent that can be learned.

This book will give you a different approach to some of the toughest situations – usually related to the people you manage – and set you up for success in the home you manage.

WHAT'S COMING UP?

In this book, I address some key topics that plague managers of homes across the country. We'll cover:

- leading your people through one of the biggest and best changes in the aged care sector in decades
- making work fun, while setting the highest of standards
- making use of the under-utilised tools already in your arsenal for many scenarios, such as assessments – including residents of the day
- embracing true partnership with residents and staff – getting to know what the residents' wants and needs are and acting upon them, instead of using tasks as the main drivers
- developing new tools for communication and information
- learning different ways of recruiting for attitude – not by skill or qualification alone – and using a fit test to recruit
- understanding risk, guiding your staff through the three types of risk and using risk to either restrict or enable, whichever is most suitable
- finding the authentic leader in you – exploring your leadership potential and style with a couple of thought-provoking exercises.

If you're a residential aged care manager already in the job, or new to the position of managing in such a complex environment, I hope this book is a source of information, inspiration and comfort for you.

PARTNERSHIP

Do you see me?
Can you hear me?
Do you know who I am?
I am an expert on all
  things me.

I achieved many things
In my life and stood tall,
But I am a little confused right
  now, I feel so small.

I was important, I meant
Something, I was proud.
Now that I am here, I see I am
Just one of the crowd.

My friends and my family...
My tribe no longer are
  with me.
My life is now somewhat
  connection-free.

I am lonely, but not alone,
I feel a very long way from
  'home'.
Help me to enjoy my days,
  and
Learn from me, about life's
  rich maze.

I am a nurse, I am here to
  help you,
Wash you, and always care
  for you.
Hopefully brighten up your day.

I know little about the real you,
Your journey, or achievements,
The things that make you
  unique,
Your heartbreaks, your setbacks
  or any bereavements.

Tell me about you.
Let's work this out together –
Your wants, your needs,
What makes you tick.

I work in your home,
You are Important and do
  have a say.
I am here to help you,
Let's take it day by day.

Life's rich maze sounds exciting.
You have so much to offer us,
Let me help you adjust.
Let's build something great
  based on our mutual trust.

– Allison Patchett 2019

1: Partnership

How far you go in life depends on your being tender with the young, compassionate with the aged, sympathetic with the striving and tolerant of the weak and strong. Because, someday in your life, you will have been all of these.

– George Washington Carver

This chapter is about working in partnership with a consumer (the resident, or the residents) in a residential aged care home. Residential aged care is quite complex and while rules have been written to ease the path, they have contributed to the complexity. These rules – government regulations – around how to run an aged care home were originally written in the *Aged Care Act 1997* and the *Quality of Care Principles 1997*, and significant changes were introduced in July 2019.

Since the *Aged Care Act 1997* and associated rules were written, the world has changed. People who enter aged care today, as well as their relatives, have different expectations to what they would have had 24-plus years ago. The expectations of residents in the wider community have also changed, and therefore the product of residential aged care needs to change. For you, in the home you manage, this means working smarter to design great care and great services that perhaps were not even thought about in 1997.

Firstly, the rules have to be followed. The rules are fairly prescriptive, and always have been, but you have to follow these new rules with a different slant.

In the past, the rules said, 'You must work this way.' Now, the rules say, 'The resident is absolutely at the centre of everything you do.'

The number-one rule – and the number-one change – in the regulations is about the resident living the life they choose. It was never articulated before in this way.

If you don't follow the rules, you won't meet a minimum standard of care and services. If you're discovered doing this, you will be penalised – not only from a regulatory point of view, but in terms of the residents' expectation of your business. Your business and your reputation may be damaged. However, if you're able to be flexible and agile, you can get ahead of others including your competition. This isn't a bleak outlook by any means. This is an opportunity to follow the rules and change.

The main regulations were changed with new rules coming into effect in July 2019 – when the industry moved from four standards to eight standards. The main thrust of the change was a move from a business focus to a consumer focus. There were other significant changes that I'll discuss as we progress. They are outlined in the *Aged Care Act* and *Quality of Care Principles* too.

The Royal Commission into Aged Care Quality and Safety provided an unprecedented platform for our industry to hear the expectations of the community. It's important that you remember that the Royal Commission came about due to a distraught family – that of Mr Robert Spriggs (known as Bob Spriggs). On 8 February 2019, Bob's wife Barbara gave evidence to the Royal Commission of his experience while a resident at Oakden, South Australia. Her statement reads:

> There is so much more that I could refer to which points to the fact that Bob and the other residents at Oakden were not given the care, dignity and respect to which they were entitled. The accommodation at Oakden, for example, was like something from the 19th century. When I visited Bob, I was let into his bare locked room where he was lying on a bed with just a sheet underneath him. There was no seat on his toilet, and only paper towels in the bathroom. He was in there on his own. It was like a prison. While at Oakden, Bob was given medication to sedate him, and other patients at Oakden also appeared sedated. I felt strongly that this was done by staff to ease the management of residents, rather than for a true concern for their needs and welfare.[2]

Barbara's tenacity to be heard so others would avoid similar experiences was the catalyst for the government to bring about the Royal Commission.

What's in this chapter?

We'll cover three elements in this chapter. First of all, we're going to look at what's changed around the regulations. Then we'll move on to a critical part of the change – how do you create a partnership with your residents? Finally, we'll discuss how we change the way we work to suit the residents' needs and the new rules.

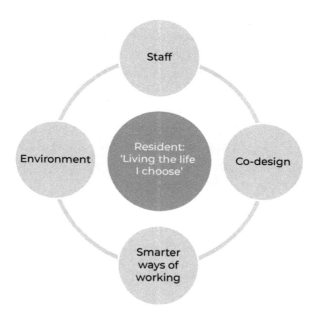

HOW THE RULES HAVE CHANGED

When the legislation changed in July 2019, eight standards came into operation – a move away from the previous four standards. The four standards were designed in 1997 and didn't connect to one another. The new eight standards are now interconnected.

Residential aged care is funded and regulated by the Commonwealth Government; Victoria has the largest public service residential aged care portfolio in Australia.

The eight standards

Let's take a look at each of the eight standards:

- **Standard one** is consumer dignity and choice – putting the consumer at the centre of everything you do. You might say, 'We've always done that,' but this has not been underpinned by a structure, measurement framework or requirements.

- **Standard two** is around ongoing assessments and planning with the residents – the consumers. There were assessments and planning in the past, but we're now moving from assessments and planning completed by clinical staff to assessment and planning with the resident, who will have the final input into what happens to them. Their relatives will step in and play their part if they cannot make that decision due to, say, a cognitive decline.

- **Standard three** is about personal care and clinical care. This standard now takes into account how the resident wants the care and services to be delivered, and shapes the way the home runs. You can already see how partnership is coming into the language.

- **Standard four** is about services and supports for daily living. This standard is concerned with creating a home that accommodates the way residents want to have services delivered to fulfil their days. The things that are meaningful to them in their lives shouldn't stop as soon as they walk through the door. So how are you going to do that? The services and supports for daily living have to encompass all of what makes life meaningful to your residents. If you have 100 people in the home you manage, and they are all driven (or have been driven) by different things, that is a big challenge to harness. We will talk about that as we progress through the book.

- **Standard five** is about the organisational service environment. This is how the home is set up and run. This now involves the residents' input. Before the new rules were in place, managers would set things up without input from their residents.
An example of this is furniture placement. In my professional life, I have walked into many homes and observed chairs lining the walls in the lounge area. You don't sit like that at home, and you don't have the television blaring for no good reason. How are you going to set your home up? How do you deliver meals? What time is the meal delivered? What does the food look like? What sort of furniture do you have? Is it furnishing your residents feel happy to use, or is it modern furniture that you would never buy? These questions give you a taste of how this standard comes into play.

- **Standard six** is feedback and complaints. Everyone has always said, 'We welcome feedback, we will act on complaints – it's part of what we do.' Now there is a whole standard that measures and monitors what we do as an industry. It's a brand-new, standalone standard, which gives more weight to the residents' voices.

- **Standard seven** is concerned with human resources. A focus now exists on having the right number of people with the right skills in your home. This has always been part of the conversation, but it's been a bone of contention. In acute care, there are absolute areas that demand ratios – one nurse to a set number of patients. This also occurs in public aged care. In non-public aged care, there has always been an argument on both sides for and against the need for ratios. Those not in favour will say you don't need ratios because it's going to cost too much – and this isn't a hospital, it's a home. Yet, when you look at the profile of the funding for aged care, it tells you that a lot of people don't live in aged care for very long because they are sick, and they are old. Therefore, that would mean you need skilled people and the right amount of people to match the resident cohort you have, regardless of their age or circumstances.

- **Standard eight** is organisational governance. There are strong rules about holding the board and executive to account. Before, this was encompassed in standard one – leadership – but there was no direct correlation between the residents' experiences and the group of people responding – those who would be held accountable and responsible. Now, this standard gives us that assurance. It's about holding the board and executive to account, ensuring that organisations have systems, policies and processes in place to guide their business according to the new rules. Ultimately, this allows the residents' voices to be heard.

As I mentioned earlier, these eight standards are interconnected, whereas the previous four standards stood in isolation; they were siloed. Standard one and standard eight are almost like arms that wrap around the other standards. Standard one tells us that the residents must live the life they choose. Standard eight tells us we need the right processes in place – we need the right governance to make that happen, and there are people who are accountable. This interconnectedness is a positive move for the consumer.

What the standards mean for aged care management

These reforms signal a changing philosophy in the federal government, in the industry itself, and, obviously, in the expectations of the people who are going to use aged care services.

The changes are significant, and they require agility, innovation and good management to implement. If you don't understand them or implement change to follow them, you cannot deliver the care and service you're supposed to. You cannot be compliant, and you cannot satisfy the needs and wants of your residents.

If you do follow these regulations, you'll create an environment that is welcoming – and that is a change for the good. If you are agile and embrace these changes you'll not only benefit your residents, but staff will want to work at your home. Your reputation will speak for itself.

I've been in health for over 40 years and worked in aged care for 14 years. I see the changes as a significant shift. Cast your mind back to around the late 1990s, when you heard stories of kerosene baths and sheep dip, because that was the way you treated old people. Homes were run on rules and regulations that were not resident-focused.

These new standards signify a huge change of philosophy; it's the mind shift that you need as a manager, and as an aged care provider, to make your business work.

In 2007 I worked in the public service, in complaints and compliance for the Commonwealth Government, which gave me a great overview of the industry. Aged care managers didn't come to our attention because they were fantastic people; they were reported or noticed because there was a complaint against them, or some kind of noncompliance from their service. My role gave me interesting insights into the nature of people's opinions; that complaints can be unfounded; how hard it is to work in aged care; and the things that were clearly not working in the industry.

I saw a huge variation in practice and in resident results – the outcomes that people hoped to achieve. The worst part was that, in many cases, residents were being neglected and were at severe risk. Even the best providers received complaints, and it usually came down to the fact that residents were not at the heart of the business. It was all about how to be compliant; how to tick a box; how to satisfy an assessor. The resident was almost a by-product of that process.

Today, I work as a consultant and have a similar overview. I see that most homes do need to change to catch up with the new philosophy. Aged care is an industry that always seems to be playing catch-up, rather than being ahead of the curve. That said, there *are* some providers that are ahead of the curve and are doing really well. Some, however, are still holding on to the 1997 rules, and it will take a huge, concentrated effort to catch up.

A lot of managers and providers think they are ahead of the curve – that they're already doing everything that is required of them under the new standards. As a manager, you may be doing some of what is required; but most people I've worked with do not have this entirely in hand, and they end up in a crisis. We've just seen – especially in Melbourne – the crisis of COVID-19 in aged care. Two-thirds of the deaths in Australia through our COVID-19 period have been in residential aged care.[3] It is starkly apparent that COVID-19 was not something that we, as an industry, were prepared for – and it had disastrous consequences.

How can I take action?

Exercise 1

When people say to me that they're already doing what they need to be doing, or at least some of it, I suggest that they need to take a closer look at which of the new standards they are actually complying with, in reality.

Take a few minutes over the next week to simply sit in the lounge room, or a space where residents and staff usually interact, and observe what is going on. Consider the following questions:

- Are the residents active?
- Are the residents alert and engaged?
- Are the staff talking to the residents?

You might feel that your presence in the room means people will change their behaviour because they can see you watching. However, I have done this in multiple homes, for multiple hours – looking at different things, conducting an observational audit – and I've noticed that, after a while, I become part of the furniture. Staff will forget that you're there and revert to what comes naturally to them. You will see how the staff talk to the residents. You will see staff walking out of the room and leaving the residents bored, and if you observe this regularly you may realise that this is the norm.

Afterwards, you may like to take some time to reflect on what you have seen. Try not to be confronted, but instead use the experience in a positive way. Here are some things you can do:

- go for a walk
- talk to a friend
- discuss your observations with a colleague
- write a list of action points.

If you do talk to a colleague, ask them what they see. Suggest that they do this exercise, too, and then you can compare your observations. Write down what you've both seen and make a list of what you need to do next.

When I have suggested this activity to people, one of the first things I hear is, 'I'm too busy for that. I can't sit and observe for that long. I'll get someone else to do it.' If this is what you're thinking, I'll challenge you on that. Are you *really* too busy for this kind of activity? Do you feel foolish just sitting there? If so, put aside the thoughts that crowd your head and ask yourself, 'What am I too busy doing that takes me away from looking at my core business?' If you don't know what's going on in the home you manage, you can't make a change. This simple step will save hours later on and inform you better than any meeting will do.

As a consultant, I always suggest that I focus my observation in some way, because having someone strange sitting in the home can be quite alarming. I often suggest that I look at the dining experience, then go at lunchtime and sit among the people to observe what goes on. It's amazing what the dining experience says about the home as a whole. Dining should be a great event in your day, whether it's breakfast, lunch or dinner. You may be amazed at some of the things you observe.

CREATING A PARTNERSHIP: CO-DESIGN

For the partnership model to work, the industry needs to move towards a co-design approach. So, what is co-design? It is working with residents to design change or mould the care and services that happen day-in and day-out. It's an approach that requires you and your staff to think differently and design care and services *with* residents, rather than *for* residents. It's not just designing a program and saying to a bunch of residents, 'Would you be happy with this?' We talked earlier about the residents' passion and meaningful lives before they came in to your care. Have you followed that through? How did you go about finding out about your residents' former lives? How would they like to see their former lives continued and reflected in the care and services they receive in your home? This is co-design.

Taking this approach also determines the success of your business. Designing great care and services is the basic tenet of any good practice, and the core of the new regulations. If you fail to do this, you're designing care and services to suit yourself and your staff.

If you do not get the residents involved, it's not about the residents; it's what you *think* is about the residents.

The benefits of embracing co-design are twofold:

1. It's for the resident. You have input into your daily life, and this shouldn't stop when you're entering an aged care home.

2. You give your staff the space to make some decisions about how the day is run. When decisions are made in partnership with the residents, it brings joy to everybody's day – so much better than just following routine and repetition.

The following example is not related to healthcare, but it's a good example of co-design's power. The CEO of a bank encouraged his staff to think beyond the bank's products. They realised that no-one was getting excited about buying a mortgage, and their product was the mortgage. The true excitement was buying a house. So, they went back to the drawing board, spent some time with their customers and discovered that the dream of buying a house starts way before a mortgage is sought. No-one gets up and thinks,

'I can't wait to get a mortgage today.' But a lot of us get up and think, 'I can't wait to look for somewhere new to live.'

They thought if they could design a product that would help their customers see if they could afford a mortgage when they looked for a house, that would really excite them. This is the basic idea of tapping into the customer – in our case, the residents. The concept of discovering what gets people excited is no different in aged care. It also fits in well with that overarching standard of 'I live the life I choose.' You have to tap into your residents' reasons for living the lives they choose.

In the UK, a woman in her 80s went into a bank, took her card out of her purse and said to the teller, 'I'd like to withdraw £10, please.' The teller said, 'For withdrawals less than £100, you have to go outside to the machine.' The lady replied, 'I don't want to. I want to stay here. I feel safe here. I'd like to withdraw £10.' The teller then said, 'Here's your card, madam. These are the rules. Please leave. There's a large queue behind you and you have to move on.' For a few seconds the lady stood there, and then she handed her card back to the teller. She said, "Could you help me withdraw all of the cash out of my bank account, please?'

The teller was astonished. She leaned in and spoke quietly. 'Sorry, but you have £300,000 in your account, and you can't withdraw all of that today. I'll have to get the manager to talk to you. Could you come back tomorrow for us to talk to you?' The lady said, 'No. How much can I withdraw in one withdrawal?' The teller said, 'Oh, you can withdraw £3000 in one withdrawal.' The lady replied, 'Let me withdraw £3000, please.' The teller completed the transaction, while the queue was still waiting, and handed her the £3000 with a smile. The teller felt pleased that this transaction was finally over and that the woman would move on so she could attend to the growing queue of people.

The lady put £10 in her purse, handed £2990 back to the teller and said, 'Could you please deposit that into my account?'

The moral of the story, of course, is 'don't be difficult with your residents'. Design things around them. They've spent a lifetime learning how to design things around you – it's so much easier to do it in partnership.

I often hear people saying that residents are old, and they're not cognitive enough or too sick to make decisions. In my experience, when you involve a resident – no matter how much cognitive decline they're experiencing or how sick they are – or involve their relatives or friends on their behalf, it makes such a difference.

When you find out what matters to your residents and involve them, it makes a difference to the way they live. None of us should forget that. Even with the most severe cognitive decline, there are moments of clarity. You have to capitalise on those moments.

With the history that you have gleaned from your residents and their relatives, and through the work you've done as a manager with your staff, you will know what matters – and you can incorporate that into the care and services you offer.

How can I take action?

Exercise 2

Every resident who arrives at your home will have completed some sort of form, often called 'about me' or 'who I am'. This will tell you what type of life the resident has had, what has interested them, what has driven them and what matters most to them. It is really important that you use this information, rather than it sitting on a shelf or in your computer program.

You have to use it to create a lifestyle agenda – a program designed to incorporate the things that have meaning to your residents. If you're like most managers I know, your current design is probably something that is routine and quite pedestrian.

Spend some time getting to know who your residents are. The following questions are just a starting point:

- What has their life been like up until now?
- What has interested them?
- What has driven them?

Now, it's time to analyse your lifestyle agenda. Pull it apart with a group of residents and staff. Start with the important things:

- What are residents getting most enjoyment from?
- What time of the day suits residents to do activities?

While you're discussing and analysing, observe the interaction between staff and residents. Is it how you imagined it would be?

The lifestyle agenda

The lifestyle agenda is a leftover from the *Aged Care Act 1997*. Its intention is to provide a lifestyle that suits the residents. However, the interpretation in the industry has been that lifestyle is someone's job from Monday to Friday, 9 am to 5 pm – if you're lucky. Nothing usually happens after 5 pm, although, in rare cases, it may go until 6 pm or 7 pm. There's usually nothing delivered over the weekend – if you're lucky, you might get something on one of the days. Lifestyle is generally seen by other staff as 'Not my job – that's the lifestyle person's job.' Where the original intention was to provide a lifestyle, its interpretation has been like a cruise ship. Not everybody wants to live their life on a cruise ship.

When I visit homes and look at their lifestyle agendas and programs, they mostly comprise TV time and aromatherapy. If you were at home, you wouldn't say to your family, 'Let's do a great activity tonight. Let's light a nice-smelling candle, and put the TV on.' This is a routine, normal, regular thing to do – it's not a special lifestyle activity. 'Special' is the things that matter, which you incorporate into every day – at a time of day that suits the residents, not the staff.

I recently visited a home where the meals are all delivered between 8:30 am and 4:30 pm. That's breakfast, morning tea, lunch, afternoon tea and dinner – all within eight hours. Then there's a huge gap until the next morning. That timing certainly wasn't designed to suit the residents.

What matters and what's meaningful is *not* about the staff. It's about the residents. Spend some time getting to know your residents and work out how to incorporate meals and activities into their day at times that suit them.

CHANGING THE WAY YOU WORK

We've talked about working in partnership; now let's briefly look at the changes that must be made to the way you work. Don't underestimate the changes that are required to move from the current way of working – which is designed around staff efficiency – towards co-designing care and services with the residents. It is a shift in the way that you and your staff are required to think and to work – working in partnership with the resident to create connected work practices. It's about changing your routine to make it more like a home and less like work, yet with all the preparations and planning should an emergency occur.

Think of the saying, 'You don't live in our workplace; we work in your home.'

Find ways to work smarter, not harder. This isn't about making life more difficult; it's about working smarter and encouraging your staff to be the architects of the way they work to serve the residents.

If you adopt a true co-design approach to working with your residents, it requires a change from how things operate now to how they should operate. If you don't change, you won't be able to deliver what's expected – either from the rules or from the residents.

In my 40 years in health, I've seen enormous shifts away from doing things *to* people – to patients, to residents, to clients. Back in the 1970s, when I started my training, we did things *to* people rather than with them. People came in, we asked them to take their clothes off and put on their night attire or a hospital gown and sit on a hospital bed – and it might be days before they had to have anything done. We monitored them, we measured them, we poked them, we prodded them, we operated on them, we kept them for a little bit and then we sent them home. Sometimes we sent them to a convalescent home. Patients very rarely spoke up to say what they wanted to say, or ask what they wanted to ask. They never queried the meaning of what the doctor or nurse said.

We've now moved to a customer-centric approach – a partnership approach – where we encourage consumers to tell their stories: to sit on boards and have consumer representation, and even maybe audit what happens in health. It's moving from we do things to you and for you to 'do what the consumer wants.'

Having a consumer perspective is the most seismic change in the philosophy of healthcare delivery.

Residential aged care has to make that significant leap into the field of consumer input. It is still an industry that is frightened to be as transparent as other areas of health. The Royal Commission into Aged Care Quality and Safety has given us so many resident stories to illustrate this.

Merle Mitchell AM is a residential aged care resident who provided evidence at the Royal Commission. She trained as a kindergarten teacher and her contributions to the community have been immense. She was widely known and respected for her achievements at local, state and federal levels – especially for the provision of adequate social welfare in the 1980s. She was the recipient of the Order of Australia in 1991 for services to the community.

Merle told the Royal Commission that there are not enough activities or stimulating things for residents to do. 'I watch many of them, the residents, actually lose their cognitive ability when they come in. People come in, and they are told, "This is your home now." Well, it's not. It's an institution, and it's where we live.'

Merle's husband died not long after the pair began living in residential aged care. Merle commented on how the lack of understanding and support for the experience of grief and loss, coupled with the absolute determination of staff to make her fit into their routine of the daily shower and specified mealtimes, made her feel like she was living in an institution. She observed that there were not enough trained staff. She said around a third of the staff are passionate; they love what they do, and they are great role models. They care. A third of staff appear to treat working in residential aged care as a job, because they can't get work in their chosen field, or because pressures from Centrelink mean they need to find a job – any job. The final third is absolutely bored to tears. They yawn throughout the shift, especially when they're interacting with the residents. They would rather go into a cluster with three or four staff and talk among themselves than talk to the residents.

Merle gave some powerful insights to the Royal Commission. All the things we've talked about in this chapter – working in partnership, co-designing, having staff change the way they work – have been encapsulated in her observations and recommendations. She's a bright woman and someone who has done something incredibly meaningful in her life. She is now being made to fit into a particular way of life determined by the home she resides in. The seismic consequences of the way you and your team work should not be underestimated.

Now, I know you're most likely wondering how this co-design concept is going to work out for you and your staff. Will it put pressure on your staff? Will you need more staff to meet the requirements? Managers are often fearful of upsetting routine, because they think they don't have a say in things like how many staff are employed. If you don't raise the bar and start having overt expectations, there could be dire consequences for both you and your residents.

You might think that you're already adopting some co-design thinking. Maybe you've looked at the lifestyle agenda or program you run and had true resident input. Maybe your mealtime experience, and how and what is served, is something you've already improved. If that's so, continue. Use something to focus a change on.

How can I take action?

Exercise 3

In chapter 9 you'll find a tool to help you with the co-design approach, but for now let's look at some steps to help you on your way.

Start the conversation with a few key staff about creating a workplace that is designed around what the residents really want. Choose a staff member from each of the three categories Merle talks about:

1. those who have passion, energy, a true resident focus and a love for their job
2. those who are indifferent
3. those who seem to actively dislike their job.

Begin by focusing on a mealtime or looking at the lifestyle agenda. Look at what's meaningful, and which residents – not just one or two – and their relatives you can bring into the conversation.

Ask residents if they would be happy to take part in a discussion where they will be invited to voice what they would really like to do each day, when they would like to eat, and how they would like their days and weeks to unfold.

You have now started your co-design piece of work. You might think, 'That's not enough to drive the serious change needed', but you have to start somewhere. If you have 100 residents, it's unwieldy to have the immediate input of 100 people – some of whom might be at an end-of-life stage, and some who may have severe cognitive decline. Bring a few in to begin, and then start widening that circle as you get some traction on the focus that you've decided on.

Let's say you decide to focus first on dining. You may see that 75 per cent of the people in your home eat in their rooms, because the staff say they can't manage everyone in the dining room. As you begin to make changes to this, and the more people come out of their rooms during mealtimes, the more people you involve.

Set a realistic timeline, say three months, and choose something that you can measure. Think about what success looks like in the focus that you have chosen. If it's about meals, and you've decided that you're going to change the dining experience around lunchtime, decide with your residents and staff how the meal service delivery, the conversation, the whole ambience should look in three months' time. Then you can start working out the steps backwards from there to where you are now. You have involved your residents and your staff, and now you've started your co-design piece to change the way you work – without adding extra staff.

The staff might say it won't work. In fact, I'm sure they'll say it won't work! That is why you need to bring some of your staff and some of your residents together and start a process. There will always be naysayers. You have to start with some traction. Set the expectation of what the outcome for the residents is going to be. It's not about staff, it's about the residents. You, as a leader, have to lead this. If there's no leadership, it won't happen.

CONCLUSION

The rules have changed, and that's non-negotiable. You have to adhere to them. There is a need to change your approach when delivering the care and services around the new rules. Past performance and models won't work. Residents have to be involved in how things are designed and delivered. The way your staff work and the philosophy of the concept of coming to work and working in a residential home has to change. Throw away any preconceptions.

Get yourself into the right mindset. Go out and find your focus, then set an expectation. Find out what your residents and staff want around that expectation and then determine what success looks like. Put some measurements in place.

What's coming up?

The next chapter is about tasks and routine. I've chosen the shower list because it's one of the most prominent lists in residential aged care. The task sometimes becomes more important than the residents themselves. The core challenge from this is making change happen now that you have the right mindset. Look at the shower list – look at all the lists – and figure out how to make it more resident-focused.

2: The shower list

No-one cares how much you know
until they know how much you care.

– Theodore Roosevelt

Entering residential aged care as a consultant, I observe that tasks drive the day. In many ways, the tasks in residential aged care have become more important than the residents themselves. The shower list – the order in which residents are aided to shower – is an example of a task list. I could have chosen the linen trolley list, the bed-changing list, the feeding list or any of the others. As you know, there are lists upon lists in aged care! I've chosen to focus on the shower list in this chapter, because it appears in all of the aged care homes I've visited.

In chapter 1, we talked about the resident living the life they choose. Your residents don't choose to live their lives by a group of tasks. Because the tasks take precedence over your staff members' ability to be agile and follow a leader, they tend to gravitate to a list – because it's tangible, and they can follow it to get their work done.

The resident seems to be a by-product of the task.

In following task lists, staff almost always choose an unofficial leader – not the manager, not a designated team leader, just someone that will drive that list. In reviewing the lists of tasks in the residential aged care homes I have audited, I see who is running the lists – and it is never the person in charge of the area. Staff will go to the person running the list, rather than the leader, as a point of reference for the list.

When I ask a staff member how they designed a particular list, I usually find that it is designed based on information given when the resident first entered the home. If the resident has always had a shower at 9 am, he or she will be on the list for 9 am. There is no room for the resident to say, 'I'd actually like to take a shower at 4 pm today,' because they're already on the list for 9 am. Staff will tell me they sometimes ask for the list to be changed, but it very rarely is.

It is super important to use good design principles that take residents' choices into account.

The new rules tell us that we have to create a space for the resident to have choice – to live the life they choose. That requires agility from you and your staff. You need to be able to have a look at the shower list each morning and say, 'While I pop around and say good morning to everyone, I could say, "Allison, do you want your shower at this time?" What if they say "no"? Then I can change the shower order that day.' It's important that you set expectations for staff to build a great service for the residents, which will lead to great outcomes. The residents must decide what is best for them and how they want to live – it should not be governed by a list. Setting clear expectations around this for your staff will provide a strong structure for staff to follow.

Great outcomes for residents can only be realised when staff understand their core purpose.

In my experience, I've found that staff and skill shortages drive routines around behaviour. The subtext is that routine is more important than the residents. There is opportunity for you, as manager, to change this narrative.

What's in this chapter?

This chapter uses the shower list as a point for resident focus – encouraging you to see your resident, not the task list, as your purpose.

Whether you realise it or not, you have unofficial leaders in your team. We'll look at who they are and how you can manage them.

And, finally, we'll talk through how you can create a structure for your staff to follow.

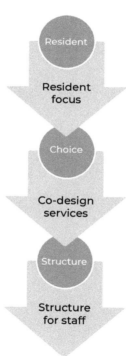

THE RESIDENTS ARE YOUR PURPOSE

First and foremost, improving residents' outcomes should be your focus. There is no other goal. The resident is your business – your home exists to create a great resident experience. Along with that, you must also find a way to create a great staff experience and run a sound business using principles to improve resident outcomes and care delivery. You must be mindful of costs, and create that great experience while also reducing waste.

Enhance the things that matter and stop the things that don't.

Aged care is quite complex in its staff and costings. Some managers say, 'I can't afford to do this', but I believe that's an excuse. Creating a great resident experience while juggling your staffing costs and all the other expenses associated with running the home you manage has to be your number-one challenge. However, focusing on the residents as your purpose will help with this – for one, it will give your staff a strong sense of value and meaning.

From my experiences speaking to many hundreds of residents during my time in aged care, I do not believe that anyone chooses to give up their freedom easily. I've never met anyone that said, 'I just could not wait to give up the ability to lock my front door and bar random persons from wandering in 24 hours a day.' No-one wants that, and not many people would choose to live in a communal setting.

Residents are there because they need to be there – usually for health or safety reasons.

In addition to this, not every staff member agrees with the basic expectation that they'll provide a positive customer service delivery outcome. Creating a great resident experience requires two things: resident input and staff attitude.

I want to tell you Ron's story (not his real name). Ron has passed away now. Before entering residential aged care, where he ended his days, he had a professional career as a writer. When he was no longer capable of holding a pen, he asked one of his old colleagues to write down his experience of living in the home. He wanted his voice to be heard, and he wanted the Royal Commission to know that his experience in aged care was not optimal.

We're focusing on the shower list in this chapter, but Ron talks about the drinks list. Ron was confined to a very big chair, often referred to as a princess chair, and was unable to move for himself. Each morning, staff would move Ron from his bed into the chair. Sometimes the call bell was left in his reach; sometimes it wasn't.

At morning tea time, the food service assistant would come into Ron's room, say hello, drop his morning tea on the bedside table and walk out of the room. Ron couldn't reach his morning tea to eat it. And, even if he could reach it, he couldn't pick up the cup to drink from. He needed someone to come and sit with him to help him have his morning tea.

Ron couldn't eat what was on the tray. He often couldn't call for help, because he couldn't reach the bell. Even when he could reach the bell, he would have to wait 20 minutes for someone to come to see what he wanted – by which time his morning tea would be cold. He felt that the person delivering the morning tea was just doing as she had been told – 'Can you go to room six and give Ron his morning tea?'

There was no connection between Ron and the food service assistant. The instructions hadn't alerted her that he couldn't drink without assistance and couldn't reach what had been given to him. Therefore, Ron's morning tea would regularly be collected without him touching it. This is a prime example of the absurdity of a list, and the dangers of blindly following instructions around a list for the advantages of staff and time management.

If they're not encouraged to focus on residents as their sole purpose, staff may think they have done their job when they've ticked tasks off their list. I've given morning tea, job done. I've collected morning tea, job done. I've showered someone, job done. Lists for the sake of lists is not good practice for positive resident outcomes. Staff should have a structure to follow, but strict adherence to lists defeats the resident's choice as your purpose completely.

The critic in you might say, 'Getting all of these ingredients right is hard. The residents have high care needs and I can't get good staff.' This is something that I hear often. The truth is, you *can* get good staff, because what you permit, you promote. If you're not creating an expectation of what you need to deliver, or involving the residents in everything you decide, you are permitting your staff to run the show to suit their routine. The shower list will take precedent and you unintentionally promote that. In the home you manage, your expectations need to be clear.

How can I take action?

Exercise 1

Allocate a morning to work alongside your staff. Observe how the morning shift is structured and who does what.

Reflect on what you have seen. Some questions you may like to ponder include:

- Who did you put in charge of the morning shift – and who were your staff *actually* following?

- What routines appeared to be imbedded in the way the morning was run?
- Did the residents like being woken up at the time they were?
- Were any choices offered? How were these spoken about?
- How does the reality compare with what you thought you should have experienced?

Too many times to count I have seen staff open a resident's door, turn the lights on and open the curtains – rather than knocking and saying, 'May I come in? Would you like your curtains open?' Which version of this welcome to the day did you observe in your home?

Did you observe strict following of the shower list, or were residents routinely asked, 'Do you want to shower today, and at this time?' How does your observation around the shower list compare with what you thought was happening? Write down your reflections on it.

Staff will often say things to me like, 'Oh, this is the only way it works around here, because this is the way staff like it. Garry might get grumpy if you change what we do.' The barriers will come from your staff, not from the residents. The residents are at the centre of what you do, and this exercise will help you determine what the workflow is compared to what it should be. Whose routine is taking precedence over whose?

THE UNOFFICIAL LEADER

Just because you have the word 'leader' or 'manager' in your job title does not mean that your staff will follow you.

The unofficial leader in your organisation is the person that staff naturally gravitate to for guidance.

Over the last 14 years, I've visited a variety of homes – in both an official regulator capacity and as a consultant. I have assessed quality and risk. I can determine who is managing the shift officially, and who is doing so unofficially.

It's important to know who your unofficial leader is, and have them onside. When you completed exercise 1, observing the morning routine, you probably picked up straight away that the staff were asking a particular person, 'Is it okay if I do this?' This is the unofficial leader – the person who translates what you, the official leader, say into language that suits themselves and the staff. For example, you might say, 'We have to get cracking and get things done.' The unofficial leader will translate that into what they want to do; for example, 'get cracking and get things done' could be translated into 'there is no time to spend with residents today – just follow the lists and get your jobs done.'

When you have identified your unofficial leader, you must make a concerted effort to get to know them. Observe the effect their behaviour has on the other staff and residents, and decide what you're going to do about it. Are you going to work with the unofficial leader, or are they ready to be released back into the community?

When observing and evaluating this, keep front of mind that the residents are your focus. Consider your observations in exercise 1. Compare what you observed with your expectations for staff, and for resident care and service delivery. You will then be able determine whether the unofficial leader delivers on your expectations.

Remember, you are the manager. You don't have to be the most-liked person; your job is to direct the day and make sure that your residents' wishes to live the lives they choose are carried out. This is why it's so important that you understand which lists are driving the day, and who the unofficial leader is in dictating those lists.

The unofficial leader often appears to achieve their status without the rigors of studying or experiencing the difficulties associated with leadership development or jumping through corporate hoops. They have another layer of 'qualities' that propels them to the unofficial leadership position.

The unofficial leader isn't always a negative presence. It might be someone who is trying to help the official leader do their job. Derek Anthony, a firefighter from Oklahoma in the US, identified the unofficial leader phenomenon within his crew and wanted to look at why it was happening. He saw that power was an awesome thing if used in a positive way – it has the ability to influence others. Derek said that, while leaders need to have a level of competency across the board in addition to leadership skills, they can't know it all. He said, 'Even if you are fortunate enough to have been given this glorious title as manager, you should still allow your people the opportunity to take the lead. In an industry that is constantly changing and evolving, it is okay to allow someone else to showcase their strengths for the good of the order.'[4]

However, Derek also saw that the unofficial leader has the ability to stick a wedge between a command from an official leader, and the people deferring to an unofficial leader.

Some might say, 'Why does it matter that there is an unofficial leader? The work needs to be done anyway, so it doesn't matter who's leading it.' That's correct in that day-to-day work does need to be done, but it needs to be led by those who you have vested trust into. You must have confidence that your leaders are doing things in the best possible way, without their own agenda. It is important that you understand how your structure is working – and if it is not working, why not? Do nothing, and nothing will change.

In the home you manage, know who your unofficial leader is and bring them into your fold – or let them go.

Exercise 2

Setting expectations is underestimated as a powerful tool. It creates a focus that isn't a list.

Create a daily huddle – a short meeting of five to ten minutes each morning – to concentrate the day's planning. Ask the following questions:

- Are we ready for today?
- Who needs our care in a particular way today?
- What are our priorities for today?
- What do we need to do to be ready for tomorrow?

The daily huddle must include all your key people – this shifts the attention off the multitude of lists, because you're focusing your staff on your residents and the here and now.

You might think you're too busy for a daily huddle; but for 10 minutes every day, make time. It's so important to set the day up. If you don't start the day with yourself as the leader, your unofficial leader will take control and your lists will become prevalent.

The day has to be set up in the right way. This simple touchpoint each morning will set you and your staff on the right course. Then, as the day goes on, you can check in by asking:

- How are we doing?
- Are we going against the focus we've set today?
- How is Mrs or Mr So-and-So? We said they needed our special care in a certain way today.

This creates a language that is not present if you don't have a focus and set your expectations.

CREATING A STRUCTURE

The huddle gives your team a focus and structure to follow other than a shower list. All things need process and flow – but in a way that is not siloed into lists. Your staff need boundaries to know what's expected of them from the resident, and from you as the leader and manager – and what they need to achieve by the end of their shift. However, creating a place where staff feel comfortable and are able to shine is equally important. Managers often see this as a seesaw, with 'control' at one end and 'freedom' at the other. Your leadership is required to develop your staff and to make decisions with organisational discipline – to balance the seesaw.

Remember, the residents' experience is important to how your business runs, so you must make processes and workflows work around the residents – not the staff. The old shower list supports staff efficiency, not resident needs and wants.

If you had 30 guests staying at your house and you were snowed in, you wouldn't dream of saying to them, 'Okay, all of you in the shower, one after the other. Then we'll have morning tea, and then we'll watch TV until lunchtime.' Assuming you cared about your guests, instead you might say, 'Do you all want to shower today? At what time? I'm going to serve lunch at 1 pm. Would you like us to structure what you're doing around that today?' You wouldn't think of regimenting your 30 guests, so why do you feel you have to regiment a group of older people? These older people are experienced. They know themselves better than anybody else. They are experts on themselves. So why tell them what to do? Having a process and structure that is non-regimental is important.

Working in a structured approach will give you an outline of how the day will go – but not in a restrictive way.

I've observed that some managers think it's more important to know what their staff are doing and where they are, rather than what their residents want and how their day pans out. Trust has to come into the relationship between manager and staff far more than it is now – but this will only happen if your expectations are explicit and you communicate the outcomes that are to be achieved each day.

In most homes, staff have a handover between one shift and another. They go off and attend to their lists. Managers on the whole feel comfortable with this because it's tangible. It's a way to show answers to questions such as, 'Has Mr X had a shower? Has Mrs Y had her bed changed?'

Back to having 30 guests in your house – you wouldn't go around asking your guests, 'Have you been to the toilet? Have you had a shower?' You would expect that some normality of life will seep into the day and your guests will be able to say, 'I think I need to do this. I think I need to do that.' Your family members that are helping you will hopefully also be on the ball and say, 'Jenny wants this' or 'Jenny is hungry.'

A list will not give you the answer to whether your residents' real needs and wants have been satisfied.

I'm not suggesting the shower list is thrown out; I'm suggesting that we use it as a guide and a point of conversation, rather than a regimented truth. The list does not help you in developing your staff; neither does it grow the trust between you. Working in a structured approach with a regimented list does not enable positive resident outcomes. The list typifies a lack of trust and a low expectation of your staff.

For a bit of perspective, let's take a look at a couple of non-health-related organisations that we have all heard of and perhaps subscribed to or used.

Netflix is a company that has received a lot of press coverage for its hands-off management approach.[5] Its leaders assume that people do their best work when they don't have to ask for approval at every turn. Employees are encouraged to share ideas and openly argue their points of view. It takes a mature team who can really understand each other to argue a point respectfully. There is a catch with Netflix's approach: staff freedoms are not there just in case they want to use them; they are *expected* to use them. This, Netflix says, is how people learn: by taking freedoms, people make mistakes, and they learn. I have not come across a team like that in residential aged care to date.

Now let's take a look at a passenger airline: Alaska Airlines. The airline industry, like aged care, is highly regulated with a focus on safety. Back in the 1990s, Alaska Airlines was a small company. Frontline employees were encouraged to make real-time decisions to better serve customers and maintain a competitive advantage; they were told to 'trust their gut'.[6]

However, employees did not have a clear sense of the structure around what was expected. In 2000, a plane crashed with 261 people on board, killing 88 people. Structure and independent decision-making came in the form of 600 employees being dispatched to help, using their initiative to make things work in the short term for the families and other passengers: organising hotel rooms, food, clothes and so on.

This tragedy changed the culture of the company. Afterwards, leaders went into safety mode, hiring 200 additional maintenance workers. Then, the terrorist attacks of September 11 caused a downturn in the industry. The company continued to focus on safety, and on efficiency. Unfortunately, in doing so, it completely snuffed out the decision autonomy that staff previously had.

When leaders sat down with employees and asked them what they had learned and how the company needed to change, they found that employees felt the levels of control were stifling – tying their hands and creating frustration. It had been about preserving the airline's on-time take-off records to the detriment of all else.

Through this experience, the airline learned that the sweet spot was to give employees 'enough knowledge to align his or her decisions with the organization's needs and plans.' On the back of this the airline developed a comprehensive training program with an explicit goal of helping frontline employees internalise its service standards and ways of working.

Alaska Airlines moved to a regimented way of following the lists, to the detriment of its passenger experience. Netflix has almost no rules and a very mature team. It takes you, as the leader, to work out, in the home you manage, what type of team you have created and how the team will pitch themselves.

Don't stick with your regimented list, but equally don't give your staff carte blanche. Work out something that fits with the residents and staff to create a homelike environment where things flow and processes are in place. If Joe doesn't want his shower at 9 am and would like to sleep until 11 am and then have it, all you have to do is make a note.

It's hard to make change with routines so embedded.

There's an unspoken (actually, sometimes spoken) blame between shifts. If a shower isn't completed in the morning shift and it's allowed to be moved to an afternoon shift when there are fewer staff, the afternoon staff may think that work is being offloaded onto them, or that perhaps the morning staff are lazy. This brings the conversation to the staff again, rather than the residents. Make sure that you have set your expectations based on what residents want and the outcomes you seek, rather than staff expectations. There's no other way to do it besides speak it and change it.

How can I take action?

Exercise 3

Take the shower list, the linen list, the lunch list – in fact, any list that exists – and meet with your residents and staff to discuss it. Ask the following questions:

- What is important to the residents?
- What is important to staff?
- Who is the best person to lead your staff, shift by shift?

Ask the residents what bothers them most and what's most important to them about this list. Does it matter to them what time they are showered? Does it matter if they're not showered?

Your staff will see what the residents want. Then, ask your staff what's important to them. Sometimes staff members might feel they're not doing a good job because they're not washing somebody, rather than acknowledging that the resident doesn't want a shower.

After the meeting, help your staff. Lead by example shift by shift, and then start creating a structure and a culture around what the resident wants each day, each shift.

Of course, if a resident continuously does not want a shower, a gentle conversation about how we all need to be clean at least once a week will be needed: 'I know you don't like it, but is there any way we can do this sitting at a sink or having a really good wash down at the bowl?' See if there is a way to gently encourage a shower where you can in this situation.

Your staff is the biggest barrier. They may be resistant to these changes. Residents may also see the shower list as such an important task that they are reluctant to speak up. If you know that you have some residents that are more shy, make a cup of tea for you both, sit in their room and have a chat. Ask them, 'How do you feel about this? Are you feeling frightened about speaking up? What would you like me to say on your behalf? How can I alter this for you?'

Look at your attitude towards your staff around this. Think about how you can start small and make some significant changes to address their resistance. Understanding the residents' desires will give you the evidence to change staff opinions.

CONCLUSION

The shower list has become a symbol of routine and task. It does not signal agility or resident-centred care. As the manager – the person appointed to create a great resident experience – you need to know what's going on. You must get to know your staff and residents to make appropriate changes. You need to know what's working well and what you could do better, and either take control or build competence and confidence in your staff.

Your staff are your greatest asset and your greatest challenge. Don't be too busy to get in the midst of what happens every day. Make change to the order of the day, if that's what's needed. Trust your staff and create something that's different. Make informed decisions based on your recent experiences that you could share with your staff.

What's coming up?

Our next chapter is about communication. When I ask people in aged care to identify what's working well and what's not working so well, 90 per cent of people will say communication is an issue – that they receive poor communication or management needs to communicate better. Yet when I dig deeper, staff find it hard to verbalise exactly what is wrong. In the next chapter, we look at what communication is and how to use it to supercharge results in the home that you manage.

3: Communication

*The single biggest problem in communication
is the illusion that it has taken place.*

– George Bernard Shaw

Communication, by definition, is the activity or process of expressing ideas and feelings or providing information. In the context of residential aged care, it is the most misused and misunderstood word. Often I will hear people say, 'No-one communicates around here,' or, 'The boss doesn't communicate,' or, 'The staff don't tell me anything.' All these comments are addressing different forms and purposes of communication. The 'boss' might have communicated, but not in a way that was received well – or at all.

Throughout my career I've found that some people are good at summarising information and sending it out, whereas others are good at two-way, active, nuanced communication. Which are you?

In the home you manage you must be clear on what you communicate, how you communicate and to whom you communicate.

This will help you to avoid your words being misread or taken out of context.

It's important that you choose the best mode of communication to deliver information; frame it in the best way; and don't forget to validate that your staff have understood you. Make sure your communication has hit the mark. Continually ask your staff, 'Did you hear or read the information I communicated? Did it make sense to you? Do you know what you need to do now?'

The way you communicate with your residents, their relatives and your staff has a direct impact on your ability to manage your home and your business.

One of the communication processes in residential aged care is the care conference or case conference. This is a meeting held on a regular basis with individual residents and their relatives. It focuses on the current situation, care needs and resident choices. To me, it seems like a pretty straightforward process: it occurs every two to three months, relatives attend in person or over the phone, the resident is present and everyone has input into a useful conversation. However, when I have spoken with residents and their relatives, they will often say that they are not involved in deciding on the care given because they don't actually understand the process. In other words, nothing has been explained properly in the care conference – the residents and relatives assume it is just a passive check-in, and they don't understand that they can have real input.

If you're not clear on what you communicate and you don't check in to see that people have understood, you're wasting your time.

When the Royal Commission into Aged Care Quality and Safety released its interim report in 2019, its foreword was titled: 'A shocking tale of neglect'. It gave evidence from initial information that there was a lack of consultation and communication with residents and their families.[7]

In chapter 1 we spoke of Bob Spriggs, whose wife Barbara gave evidence at the Royal Commission regarding the appalling treatment her husband received. In her statement she stated:

My family and I had previously made an end-of-life care plan for Bob. We knew that he wasn't going to recover and that life for him would get progressively more distressing. We decided that he not be given resuscitation or antibiotics, unless he was in pain. I remember we had spent so much time on all of that. There was a lot of paperwork involved and it was a difficult decision to make. We had made the decision as a family. This plan was ignored by the system, or at least did not follow him from Oakden to Royal Adelaide Hospital where he was given antibiotics for pneumonia. Although I questioned this at the hospital, the process went ahead. I was so distressed by Bob's condition and neglect, that I felt helpless, numb and frightened, and was in no state to insist that the documented end-of-life care plan be followed.

Communication and consultation are at the heart of everything that we do in residential aged care. The increased scrutiny from the Royal Commission has brought additional challenges to managing staff and expectations, but I believe that in the home you manage, you have no choice – this is the job you have to do.

What's in this chapter?

In this chapter, we'll address the difference between communication and information. We'll discuss how to create clarity and set expectations for your staff and residents; and how to validate good communication while creating a process for communication to flow between you and your staff.

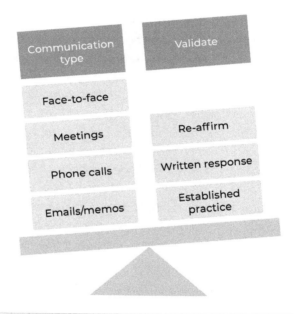

COMMUNICATION VERSUS INFORMATION

As a manager, your communication will set expectations.

First and foremost, you must know the difference between communication and information and the actions that each produce. Being clear about what you say and how you say it is crucial to achieving the outcome you seek. The key difference between communication and information is that one is active while the other is passive. Communication is a two-way process where a message is sent and received. Without active communication information is just data without meaning or context.

In the home you manage, be clear on the *why* behind your communications. Give your staff the context and enable them to join the dots between the situation, the information you're providing and any action needed. Ken Blanchard, author of more than 60 management and leadership theory books, says:

> *Connect the dots between individual roles and the goals of the organisation. When people see that connection, they get a lot of energy out of work. They feel the importance, dignity, and meaning in their job. It is super important that people come to understand why they're there.*[8]

Remember Ron, who we met in chapter 2? If you say to your staff, 'Could you please go and give Ron his cup of tea,' its likely they will do just that; however, Ron actually needs a staff member to help him drink his cup of tea, because he isn't able to hold the cup himself.

The context is important, and instructions need to be explicit. For example, you could say, 'Ron hasn't yet had his cup of tea, could you please knock on his door and ask him if he would like it now or later? Remember he will need a bit of help to drink it so you might need to consider the timing within the morning tea round for Ron.' Give context and be super clear with your communication.

I often hear people claim to be a 'good communicator'. You might think you're a good communicator as a manager because you constantly deliver information, but how do you know the message is getting to where it should be? The critic in you might say, 'Oh, there's too much information to get out there so I put it in memos and emails, and I create meetings.' We know that doing communication *at* people does not work.

Be clear about your *why* in the message and avoid a negative narrative. A negative narrative is when people speak from a negative angle, using words such as 'never', 'can't', 'don't', 'you must avoid', 'you shouldn't do that'. When I hear these words, I hear the reality being created in the negative, rather than what is possible. Staff are told what *isn't* possible all the time, therefore they think in those terms.

It is important to find a way to communicate priorities and ask for feedback. Managers, in particular, are a little afraid of feedback – but think of it as a gift that will help shape things that happen in your home.

COMMUNICATING DURING A CRISIS

In 2020, COVID-19 came to our shores. Generally, Australia is seen as a fine example of a country that got on top of the virus quickly and had low community transmission; however, Australia also had one of the highest rates of death in residential aged care as a percentage of total deaths. Professor Joseph Ibrahim, head of the Health Law and Ageing Research Unit at Monash University, Melbourne, said, 'Homer Simpson could have seen this catastrophe in aged care coming with COVID-19 because it was in your face. I think we did. As a country, we saw it coming and we took measures, yet the vulnerability of older people in a confined environment was not truly thought out.'⁹

There was a huge influx of information about COVID-19 in Australia, yet it seems communication about the vulnerable in aged care was missed. When the virus suddenly became a huge problem within residential aged care, especially in Victoria, the confusing messages added to the complexity of the situation.

That's a powerful message for all of us to consider. We now have a vaccine that can assist us, but at the time of writing COVID-19 is still entering the country and has the ability to escape into the community since we are on the precipice of the vaccine rollout. Residential aged care was already a complex environment to work in; the pandemic has added to that complexity.

You might feel uncertain about all the new information, new legislation and new rules you need to communicate. Aged care seemed to receive a lot of confusing messages during COVID-19. With so many messages coming from the Commonwealth Government, State Government, public health units, contact tracing teams and medical experts, it probably felt as if you might malfunction! This overwhelm can affect the way you communicate with your staff and residents and the content of your communications. You may start to act on bias, emotion and intuition instead of using logic and facts.

> *If I had an hour to solve a problem I'd spend*
> *55 minutes thinking about the problem and*
> *5 minutes thinking about solutions.*
>
> – Albert Einstein

During the pandemic, I observed that communication was delivered *at* people, not *with* people. Authorities didn't follow some lines of communication through. For example, infection prevention and control procedures in each home varied; there was not a uniform approach or uniform outcomes throughout the industry. This has been a big wake-up call – our canary down the coalmine. Consistent, inclusive communication underpins everything that's happening in the legislation involved. It's key that communication from here on in is about involvement. We'll not only be enacting the legislation, but getting much better at communicating it.

CHOOSE YOUR METHOD

The method or type of communication you choose to convey your message can be the difference between it being received and interpreted correctly, or not. Speaking to someone directly is the fastest method of communication; however, if you can't easily access staff directly you may have to change the method you use.

Think logically about the best method to reach your staff.
I often hear managers say, 'I've emailed it to them; therefore, it's communicated.' However, in aged care, not every employee has an email address; even where they do, most staff don't use it. What's the point of emailing a message when staff are not going to open their emails?

Meeting madness

Managers often think that creating another meeting will solve the conundrum of communicating with their staff. Don't fall into the trap of meeting madness. Good communication is very different to creating endless meetings.

As a consultant, I was asked to help a large organisation with leadership coaching – to help them define their goals and get to where they needed to be. Month after month, I would turn up with the session content prepared and be told that people were too busy to meet with me because they have back-to-back meetings all day. The organisation would pay me to travel to them, and I'd end up spending my day scratching around looking for anybody that wasn't in a meeting and who would like some leadership coaching.

Meetings can be a time-waster. Have you ever felt that feeling of frustration when you're in a meeting thinking about all the other stuff you could be doing? Or when you finish a meeting with a whole lot of extra jobs on your list that seem unimportant? As leaders, it's your job to validate the effectiveness of meetings within your home.

Create clarity and set expectations through your meeting process or perhaps a handover process – where each day, each shift hands over to the next shift. It often feels like you're exchanging very boring and routine information, but if you don't do this it's a missed opportunity to create clarity and focus for the shift ahead.

I don't think meetings should be abolished, but they should be efficient. Running an effective meeting is about categorising. Instead of having everything open for discussion, what do you want people to read beforehand and come along with a discussion point about?

In 99.9 per cent of situations, people read the papers that are going to be discussed in the meeting as the meeting starts. They haven't had time to think about what they've read and say, 'Yeah, I understand that' or 'Oh yeah, we've got to discuss this. I might need to think about another angle on this to discuss.' They haven't had time to take in the gravity of the situation and to decide the outcome. They do their meeting preparation on the hop because they say they're so busy. The meeting then becomes meaningless, because staff don't have the context needed to make a decision or have a robust discussion.

Turning up to meetings prepared and having done the pre-work is an expectation that you, as a manager, have to set.

The other thing I have observed in meetings through my leadership coaching is that it becomes a talkfest. Staff might sit for an hour and talk, but they don't reach any decision. Then they make another meeting appointment to do the things that they've set out to do in the first meeting. When you are discussing and making a decision in a meeting, some people may start to go off on a tangent. If this occurs, you (or whoever you have entrusted to run the meeting) must call time on a conversation. You could say to the person, 'Is this useful to the discussion? We can carry on if so,' or, 'Is this something that should be discussed outside this meeting? Let's move on to our next topic, then.'

Clearly identify decisions and action steps that are decided during the meeting. When you do that, apply accountability to these steps – it won't get it done unless people are actually accountable for doing it. You have to apply someone to a job. Produce action items to follow up and follow them up, because no-one else will. You're the manager; this is your job.

Involve your staff

Try to involve your staff in the decision about how information is communicated. Communicating *with* them, not *to* them, is absolutely essential. Ask your staff members how they'd like to receive messages from you, rather than giving them a prescription.

Ask them when the best time would be for meetings, so you're not continually interrupting them during the most crucial part of their day. Involving them in the decision may help them to feel more receptive and included.

Tell me and I forget, teach me and I may remember,
involve me and I learn.

– Xun Kuang

How can I take action?

Exercise 1

Involving your staff in communication is also a great way to get to know your residents. You can do this exercise section by section if the home you manage is large.

On a sheet of paper or whiteboard, map out what matters most to the resident you are working with. It may be that they were in the armed forces, a tradie, a seamstress, a nurse, a cook, an artist and so forth. Think about how their life's work and interests can be kept alive, if that is what they want and it matters to them.

Overlay this information with the resident's preference for daily items such as time of shower, meals, walks or afternoon naps.

Now, on your morning walk-around, ask staff:

· what they learned about the resident yesterday
· what they think others should know from what they learned.

Add this information to your resident map.

CREATE CLARITY AND SET EXPECTATIONS

You must be clear on what you want to say to start the day with clarity. If you're disorganised or running late and don't think about what you'll communicate in your morning message beforehand, you wont achieve your intended outcomes.

I see managers come to work seeming to be behind before they start. They may have had a busy morning with no time to plan the day ahead. Why not think about your day ahead the night before? This means that, even on those pear-shaped mornings, you'll at least have some bullet points to follow when you get to work the next day.

Clarity in your message is important, but avoid the temptation to always give your staff specific directions. Give them the context, and allow them to do the decision-making themselves. In doing this you provide a framework in which your staff can use their own creativity and knowledge to achieve the outcome you seek. Some managers say to their staff, 'I want this to happen and I want you to do it this way,' which takes away their autonomy.

If you want a particular outcome, state that outcome in the context of your communication, and allow staff time to deliver.

Cognitive bias may cause your staff to rush to solutions without taking time to understand a problem or context. Staff often think the manager needs a solution to a problem quickly, so they rush their decision-making and don't think things through.

Rushing to a solution quickly, your staff may land on an acceptable outcome but in the process haven't arrived at the best solution nor involved the right people. Context, communication and information is important to staff to help them start to think things through. As manager you have then clearly communicated the outcome and expectation of what you want.

In chapter 2 we discussed how tasks can become more important than the residents. Be clear with your staff – day by day, shift by shift – that the residents are their priority. Without your clarity and leadership, they will just follow the task lists.

If you don't create clarity and set clear expectation, you will create a vacuum for someone else to step into. In chapter 2 we talked about the unofficial leader; if your communication is unclear, someone who thinks they understand what you're saying will take over and spread a message you never intended. If you don't have clarity, staff will revert to their old ways or follow the unofficial leader.

Without clarity in communication to your staff, you will not realise success. Let me use a common situation in aged care, a process known as the 'resident of the day', to explain this. Each resident is selected on a particular day during the month. On that day, staff must:

- ensure all the resident's assessments are up-to-date and correct
- validate that they have completed everything they are expected to do
- check that the resident's choices have been noted and satisfied.

Some of the items that are checked off the 'resident of the day' list are, for example, that the resident has been to the hairdresser, had a manicure, engaged in the right activity and attended medical appointments (the general practitioner, physiotherapist and so on).

The resident of the day process happens day-in and day-out in every residential aged care facility. Typically, the set of assessments and items to consider is divided into three shifts, for staff working on those shifts to review and update. The following day, the care manager (or the person who is in charge of looking after all the care documentation) reads what has been written, compares it to what was there previously, talks to the resident and maybe gives their relatives a call. This is then documented and filed away.

I can guarantee that if I go into any residential aged care home and ask staff, 'Who was the resident of the day yesterday?', someone will give me that person's name. If I say, 'And what did you learn about that person yesterday?', there will be a blank look. You see, it is a process that happens. It's a good process, but it gets written about, filed away and forgotten – whereas it could be used as an absolute gem.

Imagine what might happen if you were clear to your staff that they needed to communicate their learnings about the resident of the day with their colleagues? They could share at the morning meeting something like: 'Mrs Page was our resident of the day yesterday. We have completed the usual process of looking at X, Y, and Z. We didn't learn anything new about her so we must be on track.' Or, 'Mrs Page has lived here for two years and we learned something new about her yesterday.' They can then share that information with the staff so everyone is informed.

'TOO BUSY' FOR COMMUNICATION

Staff say they are 'too busy' to take time for communication or change what and how they do things; but 'busy' is a buzzword, and sometimes staff are 'busy being busy'. If you're understaffed, there is no doubt that those on duty will be very busy; but generally, if there seems to be an adequate amount of staff yet your people are complaining of being too busy, they're probably busy being busy. Sometimes they also use it as an accolade: 'Look how busy I am.' If you start paring back some of the unnecessary tasks staff are focusing on and reorganise the shift, things can be done differently – and change can happen.

Table 3.1 lists some examples of being productive versus being busy.

Table 3.1: Productive versus busy

Productive	Busy
Few priorities	Many priorities
Focus on results	Focus on action
Make time for what is important	Talk about how busy you are
Champion others	Talk negatively about others
Encourage effectiveness	Encourage busyness

How can I take action?

Exercise 2

Spend some time looking at how you can create clarity and set expectations through your meeting process, or perhaps your handover process. Let's take a look at your meetings.

Run effective meetings by categorising the information to be discussed into three sections:

1. for information
2. for discussion
3. for decision.

During the meeting, be vigilant about assessing the conversation and moving the discussion forward when needed:

- Is this useful to the discussion? Then proceed.
- Is this interesting but can be spoken of outside the meeting? Do not proceed, get back to the subject.

Clearly identify decisions and action steps decided during the meeting. Apply accountability to the decisions and action steps.

Produce action items to follow up. *And follow up.*

You or your staff may take some time to adjust to your new meeting system. Check in with everyone about how they're coping and try to solve problems as they arise.

VALIDATE AND CHANGE

You may think you provide information and communicate with your staff and residents well, but communication is a two-way action. It's important that you know how well you're informing and communicating to create strong messages and actions.

You must know who your key people are to help you drive change, and who will be a barrier to your communications – and why. As a manager, you need to know who your staff are and where they're coming from in their journey with you in the home – and decide what actions you will take with those who actively refuse to follow or who block other people from your communication. It's quite common to see people gatekeep communication for different reasons.

Do you know how well your communication lands with those it's intended for? Is it sticking with them, or do they just hear, 'Blah, blah, blah'? If you don't understand whether your people are receiving your communications, you'll waste time and become frustrated. Managers often say to me, 'I've told them this, they should know it.' If you believe you have communicated something, yet your staff seemingly don't know it, it's not the right way to communicate with that person; your communication is not hitting the mark. Use a process to validate your communication; for example, ask your staff if they received the email or memo, whether they understand what is required of them, and whether they need assistance to get to what has been requested.

In my experience of managing and leading people over many years, I think the key skill of listening is not something managers do enough to promote. Stephen Covey says, 'The biggest communication problem is that we do not listen to understand, we listen to reply.' You might feel as though before you've even spoken, someone is already piping up with their view of what you are trying to communicate. People are not listening and taking it in – they're taking a bite of it and giving you an answer back.

I'm guilty of this, too. I sat in the car with a friend a while back, me in the driver's seat, she in the passenger seat. I didn't know how to get to our destination, yet each time she gave me an instruction I cut into what she said and changed the meaning. In the end she said to me, 'Do you want to just drive and I will tell you where you go wrong?' I realised what was happening and immediately replied, 'No, I'll follow your instructions.' This is a great illustration of jumping in and thinking you know things when in fact, if you just listened, you'd receive the correct message.

Covey believes that your transformation into a good communicator is never going to be complete unless you change from the inside. Communication isn't about behaving in a certain way, but also about thinking in a certain way. In his book *The 7 Habits of Highly Effective People*, he explains that the way we see the world is entirely based on our own perceptions. In order to change a given situation, we must change our perception and ourselves. Covey's fifth habit is to seek first to understand and then be understood. In the context of aged care, it's important that you listen and encourage development of this skill with your staff.

You might say, 'No matter what I do, the staff won't listen. They don't follow through on my communications.' If you feel this, it is definitely time to review your style and get to know what works, rather than communicating in the same way each time yet expecting different results. When you learn to validate that your communication is heard and understood, this will cease to be a problem. If you see an issue that needs addressing, first make sure you have listened to your staff and understand the problem. Then, when you communicate with them, validate whether they have received your message. Imbed the structure of Stephen Covey's habit in your mind and start thinking, 'I need to be understood, so first I need to understand. Let me find out what is going on and who the key players are here, then I can work out how I should communicate my message.'

How can I take action?

Exercise 3

It's time to test how effective your communications really are. Here are some questions to consider when looking for feedback on the outcomes of your communications:

· Have I spoken to staff and let them know what is expected of them?

· Do staff come to work each shift and work by rote? (In other words, do staff turn up for their shift and carry out their work practices based on repetition?)

· Do staff assess each shift by resident need and change the order in which things are done based on their assessments?

· Have I enabled staff to join the dots between the residents' needs and wants to live the life they choose, and the tasks staff perceive to be important?

Have your staff received your message that residents' needs and wants should be the focus? Or are they coming to work with the attitude, 'This is my workplace and the residents just fit in'? What do your staff see as important, and why do they think it is important? What can you do to better communicate what you, as their manager, know to be important?

CONCLUSION

You've learned the difference between communication and information and why knowing this difference matters. If your communication isn't hitting the spot, reflect and change what you're doing.

You must know how your business runs, and understand what drives your staff. You may need to adjust your communication, and practise taking time to be patient with your staff to get it right.

Be clear on the outcomes you're seeking from each piece of communication and validate that your message has been heard.

A common complaint is that there's too much change or staff don't have time to learn what's new. Enable staff to embrace the challenge of change. Provide explanation and context for why change is important and what outcomes you are seeking.

I hope you will consider your communication depending on times when you need to share information and when you don't, and set expectations for staff through your communications. Remove the meeting madness from your life by introducing structure to them.

What's coming up?

The next chapter is about recruitment – how to recruit and retain staff, as they're your biggest resource and asset. We look at how to hire for attitude and create a positive culture, which is not as easy as it sounds. The chapter will address some key areas to begin the challenge. Of course, communication is the subtext to everything we talk about, so we will also bring communication along in our next chapter.

4: Culture

Great companies don't hire skilled people and motivate
them; they hire already motivated people and inspire
them. Unless you give motivated people something to
believe in, something bigger than their job to work toward,
they will motivate themselves to find a new job and
you'll be stuck with whoever's left.

– Simon Sinek

As a manager, you probably know that part of your role is to create
a positive culture. But wait – what *is* culture? Well, culture is the
character of the business you create – its values, beliefs, goals,
attitudes and work practices. You might think building a positive
culture sounds easy, as we all have those things in some measure,
but it is not as easy as it first appears. To achieve a great culture, you
must recruit the right people and hire for attitude. You can always
teach skills and build staff to be capable individuals; instead, start
where your challenges lie.

Staff are the biggest resource and asset you have in residential aged care; this is the one resource you absolutely rely on to make the home you manage a success. Your staff can be an asset or a risk. You must know how to recruit good staff and how to keep them. If you don't recruit well, your asset will become your risk.

Hiring the right people is vital to creating a sustainable business centred around your residents' wellbeing.

In 1961, President John F Kennedy was visiting NASA headquarters for the first time. On his tour of the centre, he introduced himself to the janitor who was mopping the floor. He said to him, 'What's your job here?' The janitor replied, 'I'm helping to put a man on the moon.' John F Kennedy was a bit taken aback but he said, 'The janitor got it. He felt part of that team. He wasn't an astronaut. He wasn't anything to do with the physics or the mathematics but his role in that team was useful and important. And he understood his why.' He assumed he was hired because of his positive attitude.

What's in this chapter?

In this chapter we'll talk about hiring the right people, building capability and allowing your staff the autonomy to do their job. We'll cover how to choose the right people to work with you and fit in with your residents and other staff – and how you can make this happen in tried-and-tested ways, without trial and error. In short, this means hiring the right people, building their capability and trust them to do their job.

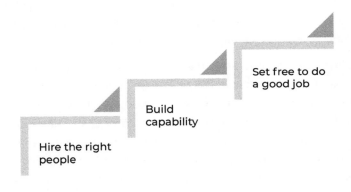

Set free to do
a good job

Build
capability

Hire the right
people

HIRING THE RIGHT PEOPLE

The most important aspect of any residential aged care home is a positive culture, which allows a great business to be sustained. The first step is to hire for attitude. You can teach skills when you have the right person (we will pick this up a little later in the chapter).

Recruiting and retaining good staff is important to the success of your home. It's important to reduce the constant in-and-out of good staff leaving and not-so-good staff staying, and to set expectations early on in the journey. Having a constant revolving door of new staff starting and existing staff leaving is disruptive to the residents and more widely in the home you manage. You need to sustain continuity in all things that will bring you success.

Recently, I spent some time in an aged care home working with some staff who were exploring new ways of doing their work. One of the residents, Beryl, had dementia and her behaviour was quite disruptive – it appeared to distress her and the staff. However, instead of jumping straight to a sedation pathway, the manager had started a program where she buddied staff with certain residents. Those staff made it their work to find out about the resident's life: what brings them to life and brings them joy. This particular resident was originally from England and was in her 90s. Her assigned staff member, Anna, had researched life in England during the period when Beryl was a small child and young woman, as well as researching the area Beryl was from. Anna used this information, along with family photos, to create booklets including simple images and facts about the area during the time of Beryl's early life. I observed Anna as she sat with Beryl and allowed her time to go through the booklets each day. The connection between Anna and Beryl was amazing. When I last visited the home, Beryl appeared to have moments of clarity and asked Anna, 'Will the manager worry if you spend this time with me?' She had realised that Anna was spending a lot of time with her, and they were both enjoying it.

Recruiting good staff like Anna – those who really care about the residents and enjoy making an effort to improve their lives – is really important. If you have staff who are not interested in aged care but are there because it's a job, working in such a privileged position will not be fruitful or joyful. When you recruit people, you must determine whether they have empathy towards older people as part of their psychological make-up. Hiring the right people makes such a positive difference to the culture and the care delivery that you strive for. Staff who come with their own agenda or attitude – believing aged care is just a job – won't have that positive influence on staff or residents.

Hire for attitude

Over the past 40 years I have seen staff being hired to fill a gap in the roster, or a role in an area that needed a particular skill set and expertise. In both instances, I've seen many examples of where the chosen candidate had a qualification or experience that matched the requirements of the role, but wasn't the right person for the job. I am sure this resonates with you, as a manager.

Have you ever been presented with someone higher up in the chain of command and told, 'This is your new manager. They have lots of experience. They've completed many courses. They've done this, that and the other,' yet within five minutes of your conversation, you realise that this isn't going to work because this person doesn't actually have a clue what they've come to do? Some people are hired over and over despite their flaws, because they look good on paper. Hiring for expertise and skill is not hiring for attitude. Just because someone has been in a job for 30 years, that doesn't mean they are good at it. It means they are tenacious;

they have worked out how to stay in a job, and probably survived everyone around them.

Here are some key pointers for hiring for attitude:

- Focus on the person. When asking questions in the interview, listen closely to the answer the candidate gives. Drill down further on their responses with more questions to get to know them and what drives them.
- If you meet someone you think would be a good fit for the home you manage, don't wait until a gap comes up; approach that person and explore the possibilities.
- Observe your candidate from the moment they step into your home for the interview. How do they talk to people – residents and staff? Do they acknowledge others besides you?
- Ask the candidate if they would be willing to work a paid shift with one of your star performers before you commit to hiring them.

I often hear managers saying, 'I haven't got time for all that. I've put the ad on SEEK and now have 25 applicants. I will just wade through and shortlist them.' When I ask what criteria they're using to shortlist, they'll usually reply, 'Oh, well, they've worked in aged care before,' or, 'There's just no talent out there. I just have to take what comes along.'

Neither of these responses makes sense to me. Hiring is crucial to getting things right for your residents and the rest of your staff. You must know how to hire. If you have a good culture and your home is focused around the residents and creating a place where they find joy, it's a place that people will want to come and work at. This is down to you.

Hiring in haste is regretting at your leisure and will give you displeasure.

Focus on behaviours

Remember when we said that culture is about values, beliefs, goals, attitudes and work practices? Ask your staff to identify the behaviours they see that would indicate staff are keeping the values of your home true, and conversely the behaviours that would indicate staff work below an acceptable line in the values you have. Many organisations carry out this work – articulating that the behaviours above the line are what everyone should demonstrate in everything they do. An example of this and a value most organisations have is respect. Behaviours above the line could include being polite to one another, being punctual, listening to others, treating others as you would like to be treated and so on. Below-the-line behaviours could be undermining others, not accepting cultural differences, talking over other people, spreading gossip and rumours and so on.

When you hire staff, you are hiring a whole person – not a work person who has a completely different side at home.

It is important that you get to know your staff and what drives them. There are some minimal qualifications that you will need to observe for new recruits, such as a carer certificate, registered nurse or physiotherapy qualification, and so on. You should see these qualifications as minimum standards, not the reason to hire.

Time can be a real barrier when it comes to hiring, but there are ways around it. You might find there's pressure to make a quick decision because you're short of staff and you just need someone. I've often heard people say things like, 'She must've been hired because she had a qualification and a pulse.' When staff shortage is a problem, get a casual or an agency staff member while you're looking for the right permanent employee. Try to think in this way each time you hire: 'Why would I hire someone who I'm not sure about and who might not be a good fit?' Cultural fit is the glue that holds your home and your organisation together. Ignore it at your peril. The more you put into your hiring process, the better your culture will be.

How can I take action?

Exercise 1

It's time to take a deep dive into your hiring process, beginning with your job advertisement. What words can you add to your advertisement to tell people what your home is about and what you're looking for? How can you reflect, in your advertisement, the culture you are looking to create, so you can attract people who already have the right attitude? Think of the keywords you can include to shape the advertisement.

Next, look at your interview technique. I have seen so many examples of poor interviewing in aged care. One of the worst things you can do is run through a set of questions that are formulated and delivered as a list – no matter what the person answers, the next question is asked. You must probe and explore the candidate's responses, finding out as much about them as you can.

Ask your interviewees questions in a way that allows them to give you a picture of the type of person they are. Ask them to describe a situation ('Give me an example of a situation where...'): what they did; what the response was; and what they learned.

Effective interviewing

A few years ago I was working as a leadership coach in a large hospital. The CEO had put out expressions of interest for a short-term role. Two people applied and I happened to be in the tearoom just after they had both been interviewed. The interviewees were comparing what they'd been asked, and they turned to me and said, 'We think we were having different interviews.'

I asked them to talk me through what had occurred, and they both gave me the first two questions – which were the same. The CEO had then explored each of their answers, which took her in different directions. She had used a tool called the STAR technique – situation, task, action and result. In other words, she asked questions about specific situations and how the candidate responded – the task they performed, the action they took and the response they received. She asked, 'Can you tell me about a time when this situation happened? What did you do?' They had both answered in different ways, which led her to a different follow-up question for each of them. This way of interviewing gets the interviewer to the core of who they're interviewing: 'What did you do? How did that happen? What did that affect?'

Both candidates had given different examples from their own experience. When the candidates were comparing their answers afterwards, they thought they'd been given a different interview – but in truth, it was just that the CEO was getting to know each of the candidates and exploring what they would do in a certain situation that could arise.

The STAR technique is a great way to get to know the candidate, but also, don't be afraid to involve your staff and residents in the hiring process. This can be a great way to gauge how the candidate interacts with other people. Your new hire is going to look after the residents. If it were you, you'd want to know who's going to look after you. Choose someone that is a good spokesperson or share the job around. Do the same with your staff. Have these people on the interview panel, and involve them in formulating some great questions.

Referee checks

After the interview, it's time to conduct the referee checks.

Referee checking is often given to a third party to complete. My advice to you, as the hiring manager, is to complete the referee checks yourself. A third party will not be across the nuances picked up in the interview and will not know how to drill down on a response from a referee. Your new recruit will be working for you, so you're the one who must do the reference check. Ask questions about any potential red flags you picked up in the interview.

When a person is moved out of an organisation for a negative reason, their previous manager may or may not be honest about this with you. In a couple of situations, I've given an honest answer when asked, 'Would you rehire?', and I have said no I would not. In one case, the person who was hiring that individual came back to me and said, 'Well, I'm hiring that person anyway.' She talked to me and she listened to me, and she made up her own mind about the candidate. It's possible that the cultural fit was a better match at her organisation. The point is, reference checking can be tricky and nuanced, so it's important for you to conduct both interview and reference check if the candidate is to work for you.

Onboarding

Make sure you have an onboarding process in place, and set expectations early. The most successful examples I have seen is where a new recruit is given six months to complete mandatory competencies pertaining to their role, and are buddied up with a great staff member who can help develop the new recruit.

In residential aged care the candidate will be expected to complete a set of mandatory education competencies and components before setting foot in the door – but that doesn't mean that they know what to do when they do set foot in the door.

Think about onboarding as a six-month journey. The first month is quite intense: what do you need that person to know and achieve? You'll be working closely with them to communicate this. They might require bit less support in the second and third months, and even less in months four and five. In month six, you complete a final check-in.

When you hire someone, you generally have a six-month window for you both to make up your minds about each other. Why not make this a really great experience? Teach them all you can. Get them to learn competencies and things that are new to them in that onboarding period so they understand they are here to grow.

BUILDING YOUR PEOPLE

Building the capability of your staff is an approach that requires commitment from you, as the manager – but it is absolutely worth the effort. You have to give staff the space to make decisions and work through any failures in a supportive environment, allowing them to learn and grow. Don't treat staff as a commodity to cut at a later date. Hiring is not about quantity; it is about the quality of the people on your team.

As a manager and leader, you are pivotal to the success of building your staff into the best versions of themselves they can be.

Your staff will make or break the delivery of care and services in your home. If you have hired the right people with the right attitude, then care and services will be delivered in the right way. However, your leadership is still required to build capability and manage your staff – to create a vision and a pathway for them to follow. It is super important for them to realise the possibilities of what can be achieved. Your are the one who can build their capability and increase the capacity of the things that are possible. Managers often see this as time-consuming but it is one of the most pivotal parts of your role.

According to management consulting firm McKinsey & Company it's critical for organisations to formalise their approaches to building staff capability – yet few do this well. Nearly half of the respondents in the McKinsey study said their organisation encourages employees to develop their skills, but less than one in five said their human resources and business units co-own learning – a practice that reinforces the importance of skill development and aligns learning objectives with business needs.[10] The respondents who did report co-ownership were the most likely to say it's been effective in supporting their learning programs. If aged care organisations were asked whether they encourage their employees to develop skills, I would wager that the results would reflect the study above. The question that isn't asked, but would prove invaluable, is what skills are employees encouraged to build – do they belong in the hard or soft skills category?

If you feel that staff development is too time-consuming, or you just want staff to come to work and do their jobs, or if you're concerned it will cost too much money to build staff capability, you have missed the point. In my experience, when you give employees time and assist in their growth and development, it's returned tenfold in good practice, loyalty and dedication.

Managers sometimes say to me, 'Isn't staff development HR's job?' The answer is no: as a manager, it's part of your job to build your staff. Don't leave it up to HR. Think about the options you have for developing your staff, and you're much more likely to retain those who are committed to growth.

How can I take action?

Exercise 2

Linking staff development to your organisational goals is a great way to help your staff understand their 'why'. Meet with your staff and be clear as you articulate what your home's focus is, and how each of them can play a part in achieving it. Provide context. When you want your staff to carry out something or think about their performance, give them real context around the daily situations in your home. You can then conduct expectation meetings with them.

Bring together small groups of staff who perform particular roles in your home and say, 'Let's go through the expectations of what is required of you each day and each month.' This may give clarity and smooth out any misalignments – for example, staff think their job is to do X and you think their job is to do Y. It's a good exercise to do and can be an eye opener for staff (and you!)

You might encourage your staff to use a planner to track the progress of their goals, expectations and outcomes. I will give a detailed example of that in chapter 9.

As you work through goals with your staff, be sure to incorporate failure points as markers. For example, consider a situation where staff think they know what the residents want and take the voice away from the residents themselves as a failure point. Use your planner as a road map; on the map, clearly mark 'Wrong way, turn back': this indicates a road that staff should not or could not go down. To reach the goal, you follow the road map. This helps people know whether or not they are on the right track.

You may have seen the ABC's program *Old People's Home for 4 Year Olds* (now in its second season) in which preschool-aged children go into a retirement and aged care home and actively take part in residents' everyday lives. Professor Susan Kurrle, an expert in geriatric medicine who is prominent in the series, states that depression in older people living in the community accounts for about 10 per cent, however within aged care this can rise to 50 per cent of residents with depressive symptoms.[11] Experts on the program monitor the residents' mood and mobility, measuring the extent that quality of life is improved. This is a great example of how staff can work with and plan their goals and outcomes around improving the lives of the residents, while growing their own development in aged care.

TRUSTING YOUR STAFF

Don't underestimate the change in culture and service delivery that good staff can bring; they will help you create a great culture. When you hire great staff, it's important that you trust them and allow them to do a good job. This is sometimes easier said than done: you may feel the urge to keep checking in. Try standing back; trust your process and trust your people. Let go of the small stuff and trust that your communication is doing its job.

In the home you manage you must have clear expectations and clear outcomes. Cultivate a productive work environment where the residents' stay is not lived in silos of activities and staff, but where residents and staff have a more holistic experience. Often, I hear, 'Oh, that's not my job; that's the catering people's job.' In a positive culture, there is no, 'That's not my job' because resident care is everyone's job.

As the leader, if you create time for key leadership tasks like strategic planning with staff you trust, and work on developing a positive culture, you are able to let go of the micromanaging.

We talk about trust as something that's precious, but it should be the basis of everything that we do. Leadership experts Frances X Frei and Anne Morriss describe trust as a triangle with three essential points:

1. **Authenticity** – 'I experience the real you.'
2. **Empathy** – 'I believe you care about me in everything you do.'
3. **Logic** – 'I know you can do it: your reasoning and judgement is sound.'[12]

These three things that you, as manager, can do and say to your staff will build trust. People tend to trust their manager when they believe that they are interacting with them as their real self; when they have faith in their judgement and competence; and when they feel that their manager cares about them. When you act as yourself, your staff can see that; but when trust is lost, it can always be traced back to a breakdown in one of those three areas.

It is so easy to lose trust, and much harder to build it.

I often hear managers say, 'The staff might stuff things up. I've let them do things before and they haven't done it right. We might even have a complaint from this.' Regardless, my advice is to show them and trust them to do the job. They are not going to know how to do it until they actually do it. You've communicated the boundaries, the frameworks, the rules and the outcome you want. You have to let them go.

Show your authenticity, empathy and logic by being you. Yes, your staff may stuff something up. Obviously, you don't want a staff member to make a grave mistake, but things that you are giving them free rein to do, such as the routines of the day, shouldn't be life-or-death situations. Maybe the way staff want to do their job is not the prescribed way you would like; they might be trying some new ways that have been proven elsewhere, but not in the home you manage. Allow them the free rein to make the resident their focus.

Ensure that you have brought existing staff on the development journey, too, because often they can be your biggest critics.

Bring existing staff with you, meet with them and encourage them to tell you what it's like to work at the home, and to share the things that you are doing regarding recruitment. Set out and establish change for all your staff, not just for new recruits: this is a whole-business approach.

How can I take action?

Exercise 3

In exercise 2 you set expectations and goals with your staff. Now is the time for you to support your goals to meet the goals you have set:

- Allow staff time to do the things set out without interference.
- Set reasonable timeframes to check in with your staff members. Perhaps say that you would like this outcome within a week or a month, and set a check-in time. Say, 'How about I check in next Wednesday to see how you are going?'
- Don't micromanage the staff or the situation; this won't give you the results you hope for.

CONCLUSION

You don't want to keep recruiting in the same way if the results you get are not what you want; so, unless you are already doing this fabulously, you need to change the way you recruit. Make your advertisement stand out in the right way; ask interview questions that will make candidates really think. You can explore their personalities and potential to fit into your home's culture through their answers. Hire people that fit the home you manage – people with great attitudes. Of course, they will need basic skills and qualifications before they are successfully recruited, but qualifications and experience alone are not enough. You've learned new ways to recruit and onboard and ensure that staff that are already in your employment are brought along on the journey, too.

Don't be swayed by staff who do not want to change and say, 'I'm fed up with all this change.' Change is part and parcel of working in any health-related environment. Most people will come on the journey with you; if there are some who won't, maybe it's time to release them back out into the community.

As a manager, I hope you have grasped what culture means and know where you are going to take this. The gaps that you have seen through this process determine what's needed. What attitude do you need to recruit? Where are those gaps in the people that you already have? Who could fill that void?

What's coming up?

In the next chapter, we consider the topic of risk and how you can become a risk ninja!

In chapter 1 we looked at the new aged care rules and the risk appetite that is needed to succeed. We've also looked at how your biggest resource can not only be an asset, but a risk.

How can you create a positive workplace with risk as an enabler and not a deterrent? The chapter is about the positive narrative: turning your risk into something that enables you, not deters you.

5: Risk

Risk comes from not knowing what you're doing.

– Warren Buffett

This chapter tackles risk in a new way and will assist you in becoming an aged care risk ninja!

Through 2020, COVID-19 changed people's understanding of what risk means – in particular, what it means in a health setting. Residential aged care is seen as an inherently risky business: it is full of situations that will make you scratch your head looking at the risk, the consequence, weighing up probabilities and possibilities in the negative and the positive – all in the quest for providing a smooth and enjoyable experience for residents and staff.

Over time, risk has developed into a negative connotation in residential aged care – all the more exacerbated because of the many COVID-related deaths in Australian aged care homes. Risk as a negative in aged care is sometimes confused with the new term 'dignity of risk', which can be a positive experience for the resident. (We'll talk about dignity of risk later in the chapter.) Risk can be an enabler and something to be embraced – this appears to be a concept that is not talked about or that people in aged care adopt. In the home you manage, you must understand what risk is and use this understanding to enhance the care and services for your residents – not to restrict staff practice or resident enjoyment. You must learn how to think about risk, know your organisation's appetite for risk, become familiar with risk in the context of your workplace and avoid following instructions blindly without a full understanding.

What's in this chapter?

This chapter will help you to understand what risk is – and what it means to you, your staff and your residents. You'll learn how to match your approach to the level of risk that you will take, and how to turn risk into something easily understood, talked about and used to enable, rather than only restrict.

A NEW PERSPECTIVE ON RISK

Understanding risk in a new way will allow you to manage your home with a different perspective. For example, a resident who wishes to push the boundaries before they die may push you and your staff out of your comfort zones. In one of the organisations I was associated with, a program similar to Make-A-Wish was in operation: residents could request a wish, and some seemed quite risky. One resident wanted to go skydiving. Normally, that would be seen as too much of a risk, but the organisation said, 'Let's find out how to do this. It's a risk we are able to take for this resident.' The resident's request was seen as something that would enable him to live out a dream, even though some risk was attached to it. In the end the resident did complete a skydive, attached to a qualified skydiving instructor. It was, he said, the most thrilling thing he had ever done.

If you operate in a risk-averse environment, this may lead to a very clinical, non-homelike place for residents to live in and staff to work in. It is something that, as manager, you will need to broaden your thoughts around. Your job is to make things work in the best possible way with the resources that you have been given. Risk is part of your day-to-day management and your long-term approach to the home you manage, and involves getting things right in all aspects of the business. A good example of this is identifying important health factors in residents and being cognisant of when they change – which may often get overlooked. If a change in a resident's condition is not recognised, a possible outcome could be that the resident becomes sicker and as a consequence experiences dizziness and has a fall. It is crucial to get these things right. As you can see, risk has many aspects and is complex and dynamic.

Standard one of the new rules introduces us to the concept of dignity of risk. Dignity of risk gives residents the right to choose what they do and the level of risk they're willing to take.

In November 2020, an independent review commissioned by the Commonwealth Department of Health was published. It described two residential aged care homes in Melbourne that had experienced acute outbreaks of COVID-19, resulting in infections of both residents and staff, and resident deaths. The report concluded that:

> *The sector is always learning, and resources are constantly being reviewed, updated and disseminated. However, this review clearly identifies how easily things can go awry and that the preparations needed for such major outbreaks are often significantly underestimated. It also identifies learnings for improvement at a local and sector level.*[2]

Risk in residential aged care continues to be regarded as an academic exercise. In my experience, senior people in residential aged care treat risk at best as a compliance piece, and at worst as a checklist, without considering the results. An example of this is that, during the first COVID-19 wave and lockdown in Melbourne, all aged care providers were asked to complete a self-audit and checklist concerning their preparedness should the home have an outbreak of COVID-19. However, when we came to the second outbreak – the deadly outbreak – in Melbourne, it was found that this had been treated as a compliance piece: quite a few of the operators whose residents died from COVID-19 had not actually put those checklists and audits into practice. There was no testing of the theories with practical exercises for *all* staff.

UNDERSTANDING RISK AND WHAT IT MEANS TO YOU, YOUR STAFF AND YOUR RESIDENTS

What is risk, and how does it apply to residents in aged care? The *Oxford Dictionary* defines risk as, 'A chance or possibility of danger, loss, injury or other adverse consequence.' Risk management is defined as, 'Attempting to identify and then manage threats that could severely impact or bring down the organisation.' When I read this definition, my mind runs immediately to see risk as negative.

Risk is often treated as compliance, with rules and documents attached to prevent risky things occurring. Yet without risk, boredom and depression can take over. Risk is something that you have to take in your life.

To understand risk, you first must understand life and human behaviour. In 500 BC, Heraclitus, an Ancient Greek philosopher, said:

> *Life is flux. Everything is constantly shifting and becoming something other to what it was before. Like a river, life flows ever onward. And while we may step from the riverbank into the river, the waters flowing over our feet will never be the same water that flowed even one moment before. Since the very nature of life is changed, to resist the natural flow is to resist the very essence of our existence. There is nothing permanent except change.*

Heraclitus was known for his doctrine on change being central to the Universe. With change comes risk, therefore you must understand your business and others' behaviour to understand the inherent risk within the aged care business.

There are three categories of risk in residential aged care that we will discuss:

1. **internal risk** – also known as preventable risk

2. **desirable risk** – a risk you're willing to take (remember the skydive?)
3. **external risk** – something that is not in your control (such as the COVID-19 outbreak).

Residential aged care is not hospital care. Hospital care is episodic, whereas residential aged care is a place where people go to live out the rest of their lives. It sounds so simple in these terms, yet the healthcare industry appears to be confused in the intent of aged care. Some residents have acute health and medical needs; some are end-of-life and need a different approach to their care; others are healthy until they die. In addition to this there are fewer registered and enrolled nurses in aged care than in hospital care, and more unqualified care staff delivering care and services. In the home you manage it is important that you know the business of residential aged care and the risks that you may encounter. You must communicate the following with your staff:

- What is a risk?
- What's an internal or preventable risk?
- What risks are you willing to take – desirable risks?
- What is an external risk that you have no control over?

You must guide them in being able to address the risk at their level in the most appropriate way. If your staff don't understand the different depths of risk, all risk becomes one and is therefore seen as negative. If you don't understand risk management well and discuss it with your staff, you will create a risk-averse environment.

Warren Buffett, an American investor, business tycoon and philanthropist, is well-known for his advice on risk. He said: 'If you know your business, you know your risk and you can start to control or enhance that. If you don't know it, that's risky.'

A great story to illustrate this is that of Harry Gordon Selfridge, the founder of Selfridges department store in London. Harry was an American-British self-made multimillionaire. His father went to war and decided not to come back to his wife and children and went to live with another family. Harry's brother died and he was left with his mother in abject poverty. Through hard work and the good fortune of meeting and marrying into a wealthy family in America, he made much of himself.

He became bored in retirement so he invested a large sum of money into a department store on Oxford Street in London. The store was ahead of its time in marketing. Harry had observed the things that excited people about shopping, and he promoted the notion of shopping for pleasure rather than shopping for necessity.

Harry was the first person to organise a department store with the women's make-up and clothing at the front, rather than hidden away. He prospered during World War I and even up until the Great Depression in the 1930s. He became a very wealthy man because of his skills in observing people and taking calculated risk; but his lavish spending amounted to £150,000 debt in his store (approximately £3.5 million today). When he later became a British subject, he then owed £250,000 in taxes and was in debt to the bank. As a consequence, his own board forced him out in 1941.

Harry did not understand – or perhaps he ignored – the risks he faced. Either way, he demonstrated some risky behaviour, and the risk he presented to his business forced him out. He amassed a fortune quickly, but this disappeared – a situation not helped by his free-spending ways, his gambling and money spent on various showgirls. He died a poor man.

Harry treated the internal, desirable and external risks in very different ways to what he should have. If he had had more hold on his internal risks and his desirable risks, he probably would have lived out a different life.

Critics might say that there's too much pressure and too much scrutiny by regulators, which is not an unfair comment. Getting things wrong and creating a risk rather than managing a risk is not an option in aged care. This creates a tight control in all aspects seen as risk and then it becomes a matter of compliance with the checklists. This way of regard to risk creates a lockdown of freedom for residents, where risk is managed to suit staff rather than residents. This is not always advantageous to the resident; in fact, it can be prohibitive to a happy life.

An understanding of risk and how to use it is central to understanding the business of residential aged care. It is part of your role as a manager.

How can I take action?

Exercise 1

When you understand risk, it is your job to ensure your staff do, too. A good way to do this is to talk through potential scenarios with them.

Take a situation such as a resident with dementia who, despite all controls, wanders out of the home.

Divide the staff members that you've gathered together into three groups, and give each group one of the following questions:

- What is the resident's diagnosis and associated behaviours?
- What controls do you have in place?
- What will disrupt this, and how?

You're the controller of what's going on and you can alter each aspect of the game to enable your staff to think rather than just follow instructions. This is called 'war gaming' – deconstructing and then constructing a situation. It allows your staff to go back and say, 'Okay. We know Janice has dementia. We know she's dressed in this way, and we have all the doors locked. Does every staff member know about this? Does every staff member understand the implications? Do all the families that come in understand this?' We then see that there is a risk that a visitor will open the door for a resident who says, 'Can you let me out, please?' This is a risk. It's an internal risk because it's a preventable risk, and you can work on this with your staff to manage it.

Alternatively, you can use a desirable risk such as a resident wanting to go swimming with dolphins, or shopping using his or her mobility scooter in the local town without any assistance. There are so many examples of risk you could think of that are desirable and you could potentially accommodate.

Staff don't often feel they have permission to think for themselves about new rules on risks: they just come to work and follow the rules. As manager, it is up to you to make staff feel comfortable enough to start thinking for themselves. Of course, there are rules to follow, and there may be many reasons why following the rules is the easiest way for your staff to work.

Recently I had the pleasure of working with a very bright, smart registered nurse whose first language was not English. She tried to fit in by following the rules because that's what she thought was correct, but privately came to me after agreeing to do something and told me that she hadn't understood what was being asked of her. She asked me to explain what was actually said, and the meaning of it.

It is important to get to know your staff and what their level of understanding in English is, and perhaps have an interpreter or training in cultural norms if you have staff and residents from different backgrounds.

MATCH YOUR APPROACH TO THE LEVEL OF RISK

There's no panacea – no one approach that will fit all risk categories. Internal/preventable risk is the category that you should approach with a high level of energy initially. It is unrealistic to think that you can anticipate, for example, every circumstance an employee could encounter or bring to your business. However, all three risk categories are linked, and risk should be seen as a whole-business approach.

All three categories of risk affect all residential aged care homes, without exception. All three categories are often approached and managed very differently, depending upon the employer. Some employers are very risk averse; some are not. As a leader and manager, it's important that you crystallise your approach and ensure everyone is aware of what the risks are, what your approach is and what is required of them.

Let's look at the 2020 COVID-19 approach aged care providers used in both Sydney and Melbourne to illustrate the different approaches. This quote is taken from the Royal Commission's *Aged Care and COVID-19: a special report* in October 2020:

> *Early in 2020, both the Australian Department of Health and the Aged Care Quality and Safety Commission established taskforces dedicated to COVID-19. The role of the Commission's taskforce was to manage strategic and operational issues in relation to COVID-19, responding 'as required to issues or needs*

which arise, quickly and flexibly'. The Australian Department of Health's taskforce was established to lead 'the aged care response to the pandemic'.

On 2 March 2020, The Aged Care Quality and Safety Commissioner, Ms Janet Anderson PSM ['PSM' stands for 'Public Service Medal' and signifies outstanding public service], *wrote to aged care service providers to give them 'updated advice' on COVID-19. Ms Anderson told providers they should pay close attention to the Aged Care Quality Standards and urged them to undertake self-assessment. Ms Anderson warned, in her letter, that while COVID-19 cases were then low in Australia, the 'situation could change at any time, and providers of all services need to give a high priority to planning' for such a scenario.*[13]

On 11 April 2020, following smaller outbreaks in other homes, a staff member at Anglicare Sydney's Newmarch House was diagnosed with COVID-19. By the time the outbreak was declared over on 15 June 2020, 37 of the 97 residents (38 per cent) and 34 staff members had tested positive. Seventeen deaths 'were directly attributed to COVID-19' – a mortality rate of 46 per cent of the COVID-19-positive residents at Newmarch House.[14] The staff members all recovered.

The minutia of detail regarding how this situation at Newmarch House occurred, what enabled the spread, what was done well and what could have been done better was given to the regulator but not shared with the industry as a whole.

Identifying, planning for and working through any of the risk categories should be informed by similar events, so it would have been very beneficial if the regulators had shared practicalities from those who had been affected within the industry. In truth, the information providers received from the different health departments was confusing, and it appears each aged care provider adopted their own approach to the pandemic. In the face of confusing information, you must be able to understand your business and the risks that are posed by the very nature of it, and learn how to think with good reasoning about what you are doing. COVID-19 is still with us; some feel that eventually we will live with it, as we do with influenza. Is your preparedness adequate to manage a further outbreak of any description should this occur?

Even if your risks have been mapped out and prepared for, the risks identified will still require a regular review and update of preparedness. As manager, your risk management should be proportionate to the risk posed. Residential aged care is highly regulated with lots of rules – not only the new standards, but the industry has a collective kneejerk reaction to the regulator. When Janet Anderson asked the industry to complete a self-assessment and follow things through, people did what was asked of them – then put it down, rather than playing out practically with scenarios of one or multiple cases, determining how to zone the home with a good flow for staff. On the whole, the industry saw risk as a checklist approach rather than interpreting the subtext of her words: 'there is a pandemic coming, are you ready?'

Newmarch House staff themselves started to share their experiences and learnings on a small scale which quickly permeated within the industry; however, it would have been advantageous if the regulator had shared the learnings for the industry, as this could have reduced confusion and further mistakes in other aged care homes – especially as the relationship between provider and regulator is a very reactive one. Risk is dynamic: you must understand it and use the best approach for the risks you are dealing with. There are no exceptions; you have to understand risk.

How can I take action?

Exercise 2

Make good use of the risk-management software you have in your organisation. Make sure you understand the three categories of risk for your home and the industry:

- internal
- desirable
- external.

Use a compliance approach where needed, such as when dealing with the internal or preventable risks.

There are lots of different risks, so perhaps you could map each risk out with your staff using a traffic light approach. Each risk could be divided into categories: what's definitely not going to happen, what's possible to take action on, and what's great. This approach can provide staff with examples and give them ideas of where to go with risks in each category.

Desirable risks can't be managed by a rules-based approach. Instead you need to use whichever risk-management system you have in place to reduce or eliminate the internal risks, and leave time for planning desirable risks that can enhance the business, your staff's ability to perform and your residents' lives. Desirable risks are the exciting part of this process – they're where possibilities lie.

If you have too much internal risk, this will take your time and headspace away from developing desirable risks.

External risks are those that you can't prevent from occurring – COVID-19, for example. Your action is to put controls in place to govern how you respond to an external risk; you should use the approach of identification and mitigation of things that you do have control over.

Risk is hard to talk about, primarily because it's not well understood. To complicate this, your employer may discourage your input and there may be some organisational bias in the approach taken. If your organisation is large or has a risk-management process that is already mapped out, it may be very difficult for you to disrupt that. However, don't let that put you off. We'll now talk about how to tackle this.

TURN RISK INTO AN ENABLER

As manager, your role is to turn risk into something that's easily understood. You must understand the categories of risk and what this equates to in practical terms for your residential aged care home. You need to make clear distinctions between the risk categories and be able to articulate these to your staff, residents and families. Be prepared to explain that not all risks are negative, and be mindful to have perspective and introduce desirable risks into your practice. Keep that context and balanced view.

Risk management doesn't come easily to many people. In fact, risk is often seen as something to be avoided because it is complex and dynamic. It's something that will keep changing and when one thing changes, it may affect another – particularly if you have a checklist or compliance mentality.

Your ability to manage risk depends on how seriously you and your employer take it and understand it when there's not a cloud in the sky. When things are going great, risk is not a problem; but when things are not going great, risk becomes a problem. You may use the rules and compliance to mitigate some of the risks, but not all of them.

COVID-19 in residential aged care was a good demonstrator of different approaches to managing risk with different outcomes. Those who treated the risk from an academic standpoint often had a different outcome to those who didn't. It isn't as clear cut as that, but it seems to have been a significant factor.

Residential aged care, compared to other health sectors, appears to be out of kilter with identifying and managing internal, desirable and external risks. Public aged care was fortunate to be funded with additional resources to prepare (the same as hospitals did) however non-public aged care approached things in all sorts of ways depending on many factors, one being the amount of resources made available for preparedness.

As a leader and manager, you must serve as a role model to demonstrate how to manage risk. I've said it's hard to talk about, and this may lead to you being overconfident in the accuracy of the risk assessment you undertake.

Don't allow bias or people telling you that they think a certain way and so must you. You must consider risk for yourself.

Dignity of risk must be interpreted in a different way; it is not a negative risk. It means your residents can take risks that they feel are appropriate for themselves without being prevented by the aged care provider or staff. I suggest having a process to follow for this which involves the residents, families and staff. The dignity of risk in everyday life is the ability to choose what you want to do for the rest of your days. For example, it might be important to you to continue to ride your bike, even though there's a risk you may injure yourself. Or it might be important to you to prune roses in the rose garden at the home, even though you may fall. The conversation around dignity of risk should not be focused on how to prevent risk, but rather how you could accommodate the risks your residents would like to take.

You have to spend time working out the likelihood of the various risks, the depth of impact if they occurred and how quickly you could mobilise resources to enable a risk. For instance, during COVID-19, when there were no visitors allowed, there were certain operators that had a shipping container, divided into two halves by a clear material, to create two rooms housing a resident on one side and a relative on another. The two people could see each other but there was no physical contact or shared airspace. That's how quickly you can turn a red risk into an amber risk or a green risk. Illustrating that to your staff is worthwhile because otherwise they may not see the possibilities.

When you focus on enabling risk, rather than saying, 'You can't ride your bike,' or, 'You can't prune your roses', you sit down with the resident and their family and say, 'These are the risks. There's a high chance you might fall. We will make sure there's a chair there for you. We'll have a staff member there to supervise you. We'll make sure that we can enable you to do what you want to do, but there will still be a risk that you might fall.'

This might feel like this is a chore in addition to what you already have to do, but there is no way around it when you must run your home with residents as the priority.

**Get comfortable with risk. This is the way you have to work.
No options, no exceptions.**

How can I take action?

Exercise 3

It's time to focus on the dignity of risk. Have a brainstorming session with your staff and residents and collect all their ideas for potential desirable risks: things residents would like to do and staff are capable of enabling. Encourage the residents to express their heart's desires rather than what they think would be allowed. Collectively, look at the risks with the residents and start mapping things out so that you have a live mind-map of the risks that are possible and where you're going to go with them.

Plan to discuss this with new residents (and their families) as they enter your home, too. You could do this activity once a month with all residents, and also each time a new resident comes to live at the home.

Often staff don't think they have permission to change how things happen in the home – perhaps they think risk is a formula that they have to follow, and that they must do what the regulator is instructing them to do. Some residents feel the home is an institution, as we heard Merle describe in chapter 1. This exercise challenges those ideas, positioning your home as a place where people can end their days in the most normal, happy way.

CONCLUSION

You've learned that risk is part of everyday operations, so get familiar with it. There are different types of risk, and the approach taken should be matched with the level and the category of the risk – internal, desirable and external. Human behaviour sees risk management as painful and something to avoid, but as a leader and manager, you must turn this into a positive experience for your staff, your residents and their families.

Make sure that you understand the risks and categories – and that you educate, mentor and coach your staff so that they understand them. If they don't understand risk, they won't think about it. Determine what success in risk management looks like for your home.

What's coming up?

In the next chapter we discuss *you* as a manager – the authentic leader. We look at how to be yourself and avoid leaving your personality at the door. We ask some tricky questions:

· Who are you?
· What do you stand for?
· What drives you?

6: Authentic leadership

A leader's job is not to do the work for others,
it's to help others figure out how to do it themselves,
to get things done, and to succeed beyond what
they thought possible.

– Simon Sinek

This chapter is about you: the authentic you as leader. We're going to look at three areas: defining what authentic leadership is; how to know, trust and be yourself; and how to use these ingredients to manage your team.

When you understand who you are, what you stand for and what drives you, it enables you to become a better, more focused leader – someone who others wish to follow. Authentic leaders tend to reveal their true selves to those around them. I don't mean divulging all of the details of your personal life and your secrets, but sharing your challenges and how vulnerable you are, or have been, about situations that you have faced.

Anyone can be a leader, but it's important for you to be authentic in your leadership. This isn't about your style, but about the deeper you – the person who's able to see that you can be many leadership types. As an authentic leader, you will align with others around a shared purpose – which is easier when you see and feel the connection to your own purpose and the values of the organisation you work for. We will explore this purpose later in the chapter.

Bill George is a senior fellow at Harvard Business School and his work in leadership is centred on finding who you are. He calls this your True North. In his book *Discover Your True North*, Bill states that authentic leadership is based on your character and not your style; that authentic leaders are real, genuine and constantly growing. They match their behaviour to the context that they are in. They're not perfect – they don't try to be perfect – but they are sensitive to the needs of others.[15]

What's in this chapter?

In this chapter, we discuss what authentic leadership is. I often ask my clients the question, 'Who are you?' and I'm amazed when they go quiet, look at me and say, 'Well, that's a very good question.' They always need time to think and reflect on who they are.

We'll also discuss how to know, trust and be yourself. When you discover your true self, it is easier to manage your team from an authentic leadership position – not because you think you should lead in a certain way.

LEADERSHIP MATTERS

Leadership matters a great deal to the people who work in organisations and the people who receive service from organisations. Leadership must always be a relationship between the leader and those who are being led.

Leadership types or styles fall into the following categories: democratic, autocratic, laissez-faire, strategic or coaching. What works for one leader will not work for another. The authentic leader will discover the qualities in themselves can be translated into a leadership context. I'll use myself as an example. As a young leader, I was singled out as a rising star, but I felt pressure to perform. I was in my 20s and surrounded by people a lot older than me, and from my perspective they had a lot more experience and wisdom than I did. I didn't perform as an authentic leader, I performed as I thought people expected me to perform and I didn't even have the first thought about seeking a coach or mentor. It won't surprise you to read that I probably didn't perform as well as expected, and consequently felt a failure. I had observed other people who had not made the grade in leadership fall into navel-gazing – a state of mind I didn't want to enter – and so I set out to find out who I was, what type of leader I could be and what it takes to enable others.

Authentic leaders enable others to grow and perform at their own personal best for their organisation and for themselves. They're positive people, they're truthful to their own selves and they promote openness. The key is getting to know who you are and how you promote this openness, and then translate that into what you do.

Defining who you are as a leader is a lifelong journey.

As we grow, we learn – and, in turn, we change. Becoming an authentic leader is hard work. There's no quick fix. It requires you to take as many leadership opportunities as you can, because it is a long-term process.

The opposite of an authentic leader is someone who controls and manages, follows patterns and doesn't lead from the head or the heart. By doing this you will most likely expect your staff to follow rules and leave their personality at the door. If you're asking people to follow you blindly, rather than thinking for and being themselves, they will not lead from the head and heart – and perhaps won't notice things that should be noticed or do things that should be done.

I observed a newly appointed leader – let's call her Meg – in her first leadership role. Unfortunately for her and her team, she assumed that she was the smartest person in the room. That's why she got the job, right? Wrong. Thanks to her mentality and her thoughts about herself, she led a period of much unhappiness for her team. She doubted them and their abilities, and she second-guessed them all the time, which resulted in them not being productive. I guess you could say she was being authentic to herself as she thought she was smart and by turn her team were dumb, but actually she was not being authentic: she did not understand herself, the situation that she was in, or the connection she should have with her people. Thankfully, when she received negative feedback from an employee feedback survey she didn't do as some new leaders do – think that any negative feedback is the price they're paying for being an effective leader. She took note, admitted that this was her first leadership role, and realised she wasn't the smartest person in the room. She realised that criticising her people made her feel superior, but it made other people feel small. That was no way to value or inspire her team. I coached Meg through this and with some self-discovery, she did become more aligned to herself and her purpose. She could see that not everyone responds in the same way to the same leadership style. She also realised that leadership is a lifelong journey. There are no quick fixes. She should just be herself. I could see my younger self in Meg, which made me empathetic to her situation. Her experience is quite common.

You might be thinking that leadership is too hard, and this can be true for some. If this is you, you may want to do one of two things: find a coach to help you do a better job or, if your leadership position is proving to be a huge burden see if there is a way you can switch roles. Many people I coach say that they don't want to lead or manage people; I believe anybody can lead, but it may just not be the right time for you.

Busyness is often used as a barrier or an excuse for not working on leadership capabilities. I hear this all the time. If, as a leader, you were to receive an award from the prime minister, would you be too busy to accept it? What can be more important than understanding your role as a leader and the relationship between you and your people? Busy shouldn't be a barrier. Developing as a leader has endless payoffs, and will give you some insights into how to have more fun and feel more real at work.

How can I take action?

Exercise 1

Draw up a table with three columns. In the first column, list some examples of how you think an authentic leader behaves. In the second column, list some examples of how you think a traditional leader behaves. In the third column, list how you perceive your leadership style. Table 6.1 is an example with the first two columns to get you started.

Table 6.1: Leadership style audit

Authentic leader	Traditional leader	My leadership style
Lead with purpose	Lead with goals	
Lead with values and principles	Lead with someone else's agenda	
Lead by example and encouraging others	Lead by exerting power and control	

When you complete column three, can you see the similarities and differences with the other two columns? What can you draw from the authentic leadership column that is different to your current leadership style?

KNOW, TRUST AND BE YOURSELF

Authentic leadership is about you – knowing who you are, trusting yourself and being yourself. As a leader, you must play a role that is your authentic self.

Learn to trust what you feel, not what you're being told. Keep a close link to your origins.

Authentic leaders use their personal history to establish ground with their staff. Learn to be a storyteller but proceed with caution when using personal stories about yourself. Remember, it's good to open up to your staff and show your vulnerability and who you are, but you don't need to bare your soul and spill your deepest secrets. Authentic leaders know or learn which part of their personality or character to bring out for which situation, becoming an authenticity chameleon. Be careful how you present yourself: we all make mistakes and by and large learn a great deal from them. Sharing some of your mistakes with your team can be a great way to demonstrate that you're human, just as they are. Yet If you told your staff all the mistakes you've ever made, it may paint a picture of someone who is out of control or incompetent. You might say, 'I made a mistake, and this is what I learned from it and how I addressed it.' However, if you said, 'Over 12 months, everything I did was wrong and I didn't learn from my mistakes,' this would paint a picture of incompetence. You want to inspire your people to follow you.

To be an authentic leader, you need to know who you are, as leaders are always influenced by situations they are in. If you don't have a true understanding of yourself when a situation requires an act or decision from you, you're not able to make that decision from head and heart knowing who you are. This can alter the outcome of the situation.

Leadership is the relationship between you and the people you lead – it's not an activity in isolation. Leaders who are authentic tend to attract more people to follow them.

I once coached someone who had been acting in an executive role. Janet came to me and said, 'I just want to talk a situation through with you so that if it happens again, I know what to do.' She then relayed a situation where she had made a decision about a staff member based on what she thought her manager – the executive she was acting for – would have done. I said to her, 'If you hadn't been acting for your manager and you had been the executive, what decision would you have made?' She said that she would have made a completely different decision if that were the case.

She was making a decision as a leader on the basis of what she thought her leader would do, rather than what she thought was right in her head and heart. The decision she made had a negative outcome on other staff. This is a really good example of why you shouldn't blindly follow what you perceive to be expected of you.

Margaret Thatcher, former prime minister of the United Kingdom, is a great public example of a leader who started out strong. She had plenty of situations and people to lead, but she did not lead her close team well. Those who worked with her knew she could be merciless. If someone failed to prepare as thoroughly as she did, she was capable of humiliating a staff member in public. She was known as a bad listener and she believed that compromise equated to cowardice. She became known to the world as the Iron Lady.

Margaret Thatcher grew more and more convinced of the righteousness of her ideas and the necessity of her coercive methods. She could beat anyone into submission with the power of her rhetoric and conviction, and she got better at it. Eventually, she allowed this to be her undoing. She was ousted by her own cabinet. Unlike Meg, the newly appointed leader we met earlier in this chapter who learned from her mistakes, Margaret Thatcher did not hear her people or alter her style to suit the situation, which was her downfall in the end.

Margaret Thatcher was perhaps being true to herself, but part of being authentic is also listening, building relationships and adapting to situations.

There are certain qualities of a good leader. They listen to people and they build relationships with them.

In my experience as both a leader and a leadership coach, the recipe for success is knowing who you are and how this may affect others; and using your character, skill and style to suit the situation and the people you lead. Margaret Thatcher didn't do that. She didn't adapt herself.

Some of you might say that you need to fit in, no matter what. However, you can be authentic and still fit in. The most important part in this is that you stay true to yourself.

For example, if you're working for someone who doesn't have the same values or their leadership style is the antithesis of yours, a shared vision and outcome is required. Speak with the manager and discuss how you feel as an authentic leader, and how you fit into their vision. By doing this you still can be authentic to yourself. You don't have to do everything the way they would do it, but you do both have to have a shared vision and a shared outcome that you will need to discover. You can use your own personal attributes, character and style to negotiate getting the same outcome in a different way.

How can I take action?

There are a couple of actions you can take to discover yourself and your authentic leadership style.

Exercise 2a

Write a few words about your leadership purpose, then ask others about what they see is your leadership purpose. You could ask: if you were to disappear from your current job and someone of equal standing (in terms of skills and knowledge) took your place, what would people miss about you? The answer to the question should bring clarity to your leadership purpose.

Think back to a time when you have been faced with a situation that has changed your thinking and therefore the way you live, a time when you have put yourself in an uncomfortable situation to grow and stretch your capabilities. Put your thoughts and then your words to these three questions:

- Who am I?
- What do I stand for?
- What drives me?

Now that you have completed this exercise, you can go back to it time and time again, refining your thoughts and crafting your words to truly reflect who you are.

Exercise 2b

This activity is called snakes and ladders.[16] Here's how to play:

- Take an A4 piece of paper.
- Draw a curvy line from the bottom left corner to the top right corner.
- At the bottom left corner, map out your journey or a part of your life such as your work.
- Work from bottom to top.
- With a green pen, mark the situations or things that have enabled your journey (the ladders) – for example, gaining a qualification, getting a job you wanted or buying a car.
- With a red pen, mark the situations or things that have blocked your journey (the snakes) – for example, missing out on a job you wanted, taking a road you didn't want to travel or taking a step backwards rather than forwards.
- Use this exercise as your own road map, and learn from the snakes and ladders. What are they? What occurred? What did you learn and apply from them? Be creative.

LEARN HOW TO LEAD AND MANAGE AS YOUR AUTHENTIC SELF

Leading can be very lonely and often hard. I advise leaders to focus on the following four areas:

1. your vision or desired outcome for the team
2. the use of data
3. driving change using feedback
4. creating engagement with your team.

In chapter 4 we discussed recruitment and how to select staff for attitude, but the reality is you can't always be in a position to hand-pick your team. Most likely you will have the team you are given. It is your authentic leadership and management that is pivotal to your staff's development, performance and success. I often hear managers say that their people prevent them from getting things done; I believe it's up to *you* what you get done as an authentic leader.

You will need to have a very clear plan of what to expect along the way, and the tactics your team can use to allow them to figure out the next step. You need to use data to cut through any bias and create a team culture of transparency and fairness. Feedback allows you and your team members to regulate team efforts. You must be honest with your team while finding ways to encourage them. It's no good saying, 'Yes, you're very good,' when in reality their performance is poor. Create engagement with your team: as their leader, it's your job to create a bond. If you show more interest in your own career than the team's success, you may not realise success and you might alienate your team.

Take another look at your vision and how you are communicating it with your team. Use the data that is available to you to help determine where your energy should be directed in working with your staff. You may need to revisit your vision. One thing is for sure: you must be crystal clear on what your vision is and communicate this.

Using your leadership abilities sometimes isn't enough. Three years ago, business storytelling coach Hannah Davies worked with Peter, a director from the aerospace industry. Peter had reached out to Hannah because he was heading up an innovation team, and he felt that the communication between the team members wasn't as effective as it could be.

During the first coaching session, Hannah thought that Peter was a great communicator. He was charming, outgoing and made her feel very comfortable. She left the session wondering whether there really was a communication issue with his team at all. So she suggested that the next time Peter had a team meeting, she should come along and observe the dynamic. Maybe it was more the team that had issues, rather than Peter himself. She attended, and it didn't take her long to realise where the problem lay.

In Peter's next coaching session, Hannah bought him a gift box. She said, 'The next time you run a team meeting, I want you to use this.' Peter opened the box, and discovered it was full of mints. Hannah said, 'In the meeting, every single time you want to say something, I want you to take a mint and put it in your mouth.' Peter reluctantly agreed, going along with it as he had built a good rapport with Hannah at this point.

A few weeks later, Peter called Hannah and said, 'I have no idea what you put in those mints, but they worked. Every time I put one in my mouth, ideas kept coming and coming from my team. What's even more amazing is they've taken ownership of these ideas.' The mint distraction helped Peter let his team be heard.[17]

Exercise 3

I call this exercise Desert Island. Here's how it works:

- Ask each of your team members to select five music tracks and three books that they would take with them to a desert island.
- When the boat arrives to take them to the island, advise your team members that they must only take a maximum of three musical tracks and three books between them as weight restrictions apply.
- Ask the team to decide which tracks and books should be taken. An agreement must be made (collectively).

The objective of this exercise is for the team to understand that finite resources can still lead to a good outcome. You might start out with plentiful staff or resources that, for one reason or another, have to be cut back. You still have to deliver an outcome: in your case, a great resident experience.

This is an exercise that addresses the common complaint from leaders that their team members are B class and that they can't do an A-class job. It helps encourage your team to get up to the A-class level by exercising their creative capacities, their negotiation skills and their innovative thinking.

Staff don't like change and might push back or get in the way, but your authentic leadership and management of a situation will lead your staff through any pushback.

CONCLUSION

Authentic leadership matters a great deal to people who work in your organisation, and to the people who receive your care and services. It underpins all that you have read in this book so far. Not everyone relates or responds in the same way to the same leadership style, so leading and managing a team depends on you being an authentic leader.

Start to share some more of yourself each day and use the four areas of leadership to enhance your team's development. Embed your vision, use data and feedback well to change and improve what you do, and create engagement within your team.

What's coming up?

The next chapter discusses the importance of knowing your residents, first and foremost. Your residents are your consumers and the reason for your business. It's imperative that you understand who and what is at the core of your business. Being an authentic leader is a basic tenet of leadership; as you develop your skills in this area, knowing your job and getting to know your residents will become easier.

7: Know your residents – deliver first-class service

Customer service is just a day-in, day-out, ongoing, never-ending, unremitting, persevering, compassionate type of activity.

– Leon Gorman

This chapter is a refreshing take on getting to know the residents that live in the home you manage. We'll look at the practical yet simple ways of providing good customer service and using feedback of all types to enhance the care and services you deliver. We'll discuss the key to getting to know your residents and how to use the assessment process that you have in your system effectively, seeing the feedback you receive as a gift.

Your residents and their relatives or significant others are your customers. Understanding your customer is the cornerstone of managing your business well. At every point of every transaction between two human beings, be prepared and expect some feedback – a compliment, complaint or suggestion. Take this feedback and treat it like gold. It's a gift, and information you may not anticipate or predict without another's input. No matter what your customers' needs are, you and your staff should be able to deliver care and services with ease, using great customer service skills. This will improve resident-staff relationships and make the things you are striving to deliver possible.

The Royal Commission into Aged Care Quality and Safety uncovered many examples of both good and poor customer service. Back in chapter 1, Merle Mitchell described her perception that some staff in the aged care home she lives in were only there because it was a job. She said that bored staff would yawn each time they spoke with another resident. Imagine if you were shopping in a department store and the assistant yawned at you every time you spoke.

Not every employee has a basic level of customer service training, but if you set good customer service as an expectation from day one of their employment, the attitude staff should have towards the residents becomes clearer and more aligned to what you have in mind.

I've had the misfortune to witness staff talking over residents' heads as if they didn't exist and shouting down the corridors as if they were working in a warehouse. Recently, as I walked down a corridor in a home, I witnessed a resident's door propped open by a senior member of staff who was talking to two junior members of staff while they were giving a sponge bath to the resident in her bed. I said to the senior staff member, 'Please shut that door and come and talk to me. Talk me through what I've just seen.' The senior staff member became quite embarrassed and apologetic, as did the two junior staff. It showed me that they had no concept of the basic customer service, dignity and privacy that was needed for that resident. Behaviour like this is not always malicious; it comes from not understanding what's expected.

What's in this chapter?

In this chapter we take a look at how you can get to know your residents by utilising the assessment process that you already have – the myriad assessments, both clinical and non-clinical, bringing alive everything you do with the resident. We'll look at how to refine the things that staff and residents have already agreed upon – for example, the nuances that a resident has expressed a desire for and staff have encapsulated into the resident's day.

We'll revisit how you use feedback, and how to treat it as a gift – showing both residents and your staff how they can provide feedback and how it will reform your business.

We'll define what great customer service is and what that means in every transaction, and how to set expectations for your staff so they deliver on this.

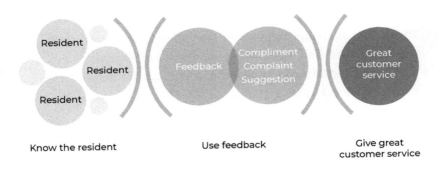

Know the resident   Use feedback   Give great customer service

KNOW YOUR RESIDENT

Imagine a couple decided to venture into the holiday accommodation business and purchased a holiday house. They'd never done this before. They went about setting their house up and then decided to invite a group of friends who were regular travellers for the weekend. The guests were all given a pad and pen and asked to give feedback on what worked well and what could be done better.

Some of the feedback surprised the couple. Comments they received included:

- If it's a holiday house that will take dogs, leave dog treats as well as human treats for guests.
- Have extra pillows and extra bedding available, because it can get quite cold at night.
- Have lots of books and games.
- Make sure you leave instructions so people know how to use the wood burners.

These were all things that the couple had not considered. Rather than feeling affronted, the whole experience of feedback was a gift that they could then package and turn into something that has been quite successful.

Myriad assessments are completed when a resident enters aged care, and these are ongoing. The assessment process is an ideal time to get to know the resident well, yet assessments are often treated as something to get through quickly. You use them to assess clinical and non-clinical needs, as well as for funding purposes. Unless anything stands out in them, they're usually filed or entered into your electronic system.

If you ask the right questions, there is rich information that can be gleaned from these assessments.

If, for example, a resident has a cognitive deficit such as dementia, who is the best person to give you context about that resident, their life, their moments of clarity and so forth? If you perform the assessment as a task and treat the information gathered as routine without considering it as context about the resident, the assessment will lose its meaning and intent. Your staff will not be able to appreciate the resident's life experiences and the value they can add to everyone else's lives in your home. You must get this right; if you put it into practice now, the new recommendations will build on what is already your good practice.

The information from the Royal Commission was released in December 2020 and tabled in parliament in February 2021. One of the recommendations includes a common set of eligibility criteria to prevent or delay deterioration in a resident's capacity to function independently for as long as possible.

In the home you manage, you must ensure that residents have every possible opportunity to live the life they want to, in a way they want to. It's an entitlement that relates to all forms of care the individual is assessed as needing. A single assessment process using the same assessment framework and arrangement for assessors will soon be introduced, streamlining the current system. The notion of 'having a right to live the life I choose', and funding based on the assessed needs and genuine individual choice over how their aged care needs are met, will be quite revolutionary. However, what's currently on offer in residential aged care isn't always matched with the needs of the resident. Having standard one outline resident choice, coupled with the weight of the Royal Commission into Aged Care Quality and Safety, will formally pave the way to true resident choice becoming a driving force in every home.

In my experience – and I have heard managers say this many times – homes complete the assessments already, but all the information captured isn't utilised effectively. The assessment may be done well, but the information collected may not be communicated well. All staff may not know about the resident. Ask yourself, what is the point of the assessment other than completing a task or getting a piece of funding? You can use the assessment for many things – including educating your staff, and turning it into a piece of work around customer service. Learn how to be agile and use the information you already have to hand.

How can I take action?

Exercise 1

In chapter 3 I discussed the 'resident of the day' process and how the information gleaned isn't always utilised or communicated. It is time to take a look at how you can put your resident of the day process to work.

Start small. The resident of the day process is really a top-to-toe assessment of one resident each day. It's based on the number of residents in the home in any one month – so if you have 30 residents, one resident is resident of the day on each day of the month.

What do you use the information for? Could you use the resident of the day process as a teaching tool?

Could you use it for anything else?

Usually, the information gleaned during the resident of the day process isn't shared with all staff. This means that not all staff know what's happening during the resident of the day process

award. The analogy used has stayed with me all these years, as it most likely has with all the other employees from that time, too.

The name of the award comes from an example of how you can assist people with great customer service, using a supermarket setting. Imagine if you saw someone at the checkout with a lot of shopping inside a plastic bag (remember the days when we had free flimsy plastic bags? Thank goodness we've moved on from there!), and you realised the bag was about to break because it was not strong enough to carry the load. Great customer service would be to go to the customer and offer another bag – to double bag the groceries for them. Employees were always pleased to be nominated as a Double Bagger.

All employees of the hospital understood exactly what was expected of them in their interactions with the customer – in this case, the patient. Expectation-setting and assisting with scripts or ways to interact with the customer does work, and benefits both the employee and the customer.

Get comfortable with all types of feedback and involve staff and develop them. Critics might say that all feedback should be dealt with by the manager, not the staff, because the seriousness warrants seniority. In my experience, when feedback is given about care, services or a particular employee, it is often dealt with by the manager with little or no employee input. However, taking a complaint seriously and investigating properly will often warrant gaining information from all available sources, including staff.

Feedback must be taken seriously. If the feedback is a complaint, be sure that you have investigated it thoroughly and have a process to respond to the person who has given the feedback.

How can I take action?

Exercise 2a

Take the feedback challenge. Gather together some of your key staff, or staff you would like to encourage to engage further with feedback.

Ask them to:

- Review your home's website. Write down what is great about the site, and what could be presented better.
- Roleplay the information a new resident and their family are given before and on arrival to the home. Discuss any improvements that could be made.
- Workshop the 'welcome to the home' process and its pros and cons.
- Observe a new resident's journey into the home, and what happens within their first four weeks. Consider that experience from the resident's perspective and discuss positives and negatives.

Now ask your staff what works well and what can be improved. You can repeat this exercise with a number of staff or groups of staff.

Exercise 2b

Consider your customer interactions. Script greetings and daily interactions for:

- answering the phone
- entering a resident's room
- addressing a resident and finding out if their title or first name is acceptable for them
- receiving feedback, responding to it and the next steps.

Changing the way staff use their words can be tricky, especially if English isn't their first language. However, it's important to set expectations early on about what great customer service is and give your staff scripts to learn about tone and consistency.

DELIVER ON FIRST-CLASS SERVICE

To make a difference to how your residents are cared for and the way service is delivered, you must address the attitudes and behaviour of your staff. I don't mean getting stuck in the minutia of teamwork, values and mission statements. Help your staff to deliver a first-class customer service experience that is continuous, persistent, constant and ongoing. It should become the norm. Think about your experience when you check into a hotel. Staff are taught how to greet you, how to check you in, how to give you information and how to ask if there's anything that they can do for you. Consistent, continuous, persistent, ongoing customer service is expected.

First-class service is important to your business because residents are the lifeblood of your business. Put simply, they are the reason your business exists.

Most organisations say they want enthusiastic, engaged employees, and with good reason. Employee engagement is often tied up with a business's financial success. Research by Gallup across multiple types of businesses found that around 70 per cent of employees are not engaged, or are actively disengaged, at work.[18] This rings true in aged care when we consider the information Merle Mitchell provided the Royal Commission, saying a third of aged care staff are there because it's a job and a third are bored at work.

In my experience, this disconnect between the employee, customer (resident) and engagement occurs because organisations try to promote engagement in ways that are disconnected from what truly inspires and motivates staff. Typically, the HR department is the owner of engagement and uses measures to report back to the leaders and managers through an employee satisfaction or engagement survey. At best, the results may lead to some staff development opportunities organised by the HR department. However, tapping into the real meaning people derive from their work in aged care – which is taking care of the residents and improving their lives through that care – is often overlooked, and not used in team-building or other such exercises to improve staff development, outcomes and joy in their job.

The current approach in aged care is just like the way most organisations deal with customers – via satisfaction surveys and so on. However, in recent years, big-brand companies such as Apple have changed their customer experience and have made 'wowing' the customer a priority for every frontline worker. Residential aged care is not Apple, but there is no reason your frontline workers can't use some of these skills and ideas to deliver great customer service at each transaction – effectively leaving the resident mightily pleased that they have chosen the home you manage.

Some may say that residential aged care is not the place to have this level of emphasis on customer service, and that some staff do not have English as their first language and would find this too difficult to deliver on. However, in my experience, if you begin with your expectations and take time to show staff how to deliver great customer service, it is not too difficult and it is worth the effort.

How can I take action?

Exercise 3

Engaging staff through exercises to show them how to deliver great customer service is beneficial to your residents, staff and the business as a whole.

Using stories is a great way to engage your staff in customer service. For example, think of a time when you have received both good and bad customer service, and how that made you feel. You can ask staff to participate in this exercise as everyone has a story.

Next, conduct an exercise with staff where you draw four boxes.

In the top left-hand box, write: 'What does great customer service mean in the home that you work in?' In the top right-hand box, write: 'What does great customer service mean to me?'

In the bottom left-hand box, brainstorm everything concerning customer service you and your staff can think of.

In the bottom right-hand box, identify what each benefit means to the resident and what it means to staff. Then, prioritise the top five benefits to you and to the home you work in:

· List the benefits.
· Identify all potential objections/barriers.
· Find ways to overcome the objections/barriers to create the top five benefits.

When identifying the objections or barriers to providing first-class customer service, give staff permission to think about what they would like to receive. Create the environment to assist your staff. You cannot create the change in isolation – you need your staff to be part of this.

CONCLUSION

In this chapter we've learned how the regular routines of your business – such as the myriad assessments undertaken for each resident – can contain many great pieces of information and context for your staff to help them deliver great care and services. You must set expectations early regarding what great customer service is and how to deliver it. Give your staff words and actions to bring in confidence and consistency. Provide consistency and develop proficiency. Treat feedback of any type as your golden ticket.

It can be challenging to realise there are more gaps than you expected, and perhaps the main barrier is resistance. To cut through resistance, work with your staff, set up expectations, give them scripts and walk them through what's expected and required.

Think about all the assessments that you're undertaking. How can you easily pull some useful information from these to make a difference to your staff?

Make sure you are clear on what great customer service is and how you can develop your staff to deliver on it.

What's coming up?

The next chapter is named 'Ready, set, go'. It's the final chapter in preparing you to get ready to take the actions that we've discussed in this book. Get yourself set, prepared, and go on to be a more effective leader and manager.

8: Ready, set, go

If you fail to plan, you are planning to fail.

– Benjamin Franklin

This is the chapter to get you ready for action and making change – large and small. In this chapter we will look at whether you are ready to take on the challenge of a residential aged care manager's job; or, if you are currently in the job, whether you are ready to change the way you operate in your role. What does it take to get set and be able to launch all the things that you would like to achieve? Get your bag of tools and things to do, and take action.

In this book, you have read about the things that could and should be done, and the things that can inhibit your progress. I have also given you lots of great exercises to try; but where do you start? How can you ready yourself and get set? What is the best way to kick off?

You may feel that you already have good leadership and management skills, yet you still don't hit the mark when it comes to getting consistent results. Focusing on tasks often comes at the expense of focusing on your staff. Balance who you are and what you want and need to achieve – and shift the focus if the situation requires you to do so.

On your mark. Get ready. Get set. Go!

What's in this chapter?

First, we'll look at how to prepare yourself. You must take time to understand where the gaps are, or which good things in your home you would like to enhance further. What do you need to do to prepare yourself and put yourself in the best position for success?

Then we'll discuss how to position yourself. What does it take to be in the best position to achieve the things that you have set out to do?

Finally, it will be time to commit to doing what you have set out to do. Don't let procrastination or any other saboteur get in the way.

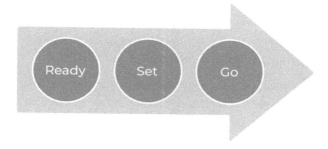

GET READY

You must be able to prepare yourself – and your team – to deliver on a responsibility that you as leader are accountable for. This section is about readying yourself for action.

You may have to improve an aspect of your leadership and management, such as focusing on your decision-making skills; and consider the order in which to do things, what resources you may need, and how to prepare and develop your staff.

Preparation is the key to avoid failure.

You must use this step in any new or existing piece you work on to develop your staff, achieve expected outcomes and complete the job you have started.

Preparation is not a one-off event. It is constant. Consider the experience of Luke Brown – a former air force engineer who decided he would like to try his hand at project management. His first few roles were in managing aircraft acquisition projects. He was determined to be successful, so he prepared by enrolling in a few project management courses. He thought that if he had a strong project plan and a detailed schedule, he would succeed.

For his first project, he worked hard on getting his project plan and schedule right; but within a couple of years, the project started to go off the rails. It was falling behind schedule. Luke struggled to understand why. He thought he had put everything in place. He asked a few senior executives why they thought the project hadn't run to plan. 'You need a better plan and more detailed schedule,' they told him.

With his next project, Luke was determined to do better. He put more work into creating the perfect project plan and a more detailed schedule. He talked through each document more carefully and took more time breaking down each component. Once again, the project went off track. The team was not meeting performance targets, and disagreements were occurring. Again, Luke asked his senior executives, 'What's gone wrong?' The response he received was, 'You need a better schedule and a better plan. You should have rewritten the plan when you started to fall behind.'

For his third project, he wasn't going to get it wrong. Luke worked side-by-side with the team. He held weekly reviews and monthly deep dives. He also conducted regular, detailed risk analysis. Again, the project went off track. He started to think, 'Maybe it's not me, my plan or the schedule. Maybe there's something more to this.' His mantra of 'plan the work and work the plan' wasn't working. He then sought out people within his organisation who had successfully managed difficult projects and asked them for advice. They didn't tell him he needed a stronger plan or more detail. Instead, they told him they had succeeded because they had built strong relationships. They had got to know their broader team, including their contractors – and, as a result, they all worked well together.

Luke enrolled in a master's degree in complex project management. He placed more emphasis on teams and relationships and reinforced the advice he had received. He soon found himself managing a project that was later in its life cycle. The project had fallen behind schedule due to a dispute with a contractor and had been labelled a 'major project of concern'. Within about a year, the project was back on track. Within two years, the project had delivered most of its capability. Luke had turned the project around with his new mantra: 'plan the work and work the people'.[19]

In my experience, those who lead and manage and wish to go it alone on the decision-making front will often have similar experiences to Luke's. It's important to build relationships with the people that matter – the people around you. Take time in your preparation to involve the staff, and maybe some residents, who will be involved in the changes that you are preparing for.

Be careful not to bow to pressure. You might feel pressure from your manager, the owner of the home or the situation itself. Rushing things through without preparation always leads to a poor outcome.

How can I take action?

Exercise 1

Getting ready takes thought and planning. Sometimes you need another person's opinion to counterbalance your own.

Ask someone who is successful in change management to give you their take on how you manage your people and get things done. Their insights may prove helpful to you. Ask them how they go about change and see how they manage the things you are hopeful of achieving.

Now, write down what you have taken from the conversation and decide whether it can be of use to your preparations. You can repeat this exercise as many times as is helpful for you. Everyone has a slightly different approach, and by talking through your issues with someone more experienced you may get some really good insights into your own behaviours, as well as picking up some tried-and-true methods from others.

GET SET

To get set and be able to launch all the things that you would like to achieve requires you to put in place the things that you have prepared. Make sure all the pieces in your prepared process are completed and everyone knows exactly what's expected of them. You have your final vision, and the outcome that you want is understood well and agreed upon by all the people that you have involved in the process.

Let's use making a cake as an example of why getting set is so important. Say you've found the best recipe for what you want to achieve, and you have sourced the correct ingredients to make the cake. You have the bowl and all the utensils. To get set, you must then do the following:

- check the ingredients and the equipment are correct
- ensure the oven is capable of reaching the temperature you need
- ensure you have help at hand, if you are likely to need assistance.

This leaves you ready for the final step, which is to make the cake. If you don't have this assurance in the preparation, your cake could fail by missing some vital ingredient or process.

When the preparation is done, the 'get set' part is the testing that everything is in place and in order, ready to proceed. Let's take a look at a story to illustrate that at every stage in preparation and getting set, a test is invaluable and how you react is even more so.

Let's take a look at an example of how 'getting set' can work in aged care. Sean was a lifestyle coordinator working in a large residential aged care home. He had worked with both residents and staff to plan a great day out for most of the residents to enjoy. On the day of the much-anticipated daytrip an unannounced accreditation visit occurred. Three assessors turned up at the home to conduct an accreditation audit.

At first, all the staff agreed that the day trip couldn't go ahead because the assessors would want to interview Sean and some of the residents. No-one dared say anything to the contrary – except for Sean.

Sean loved his job as lifestyle coordinator and took pride in working with the residents and staff to create amazing experiences for the residents. He approached the assessors politely, stating that the planned trip was something the residents had helped create and were looking forward to going on, and as it was to be an accreditation audit over a couple of days he would be available tomorrow to talk to the assessors.

The manager of the home was delighted with Sean's initiative and drive to do what he had set out to do; the residents and staff were allowed to go on the trip as planned; and the following day Sean made himself available to sit with the assessors to answer their audit questions.

When the audit was completed, the manager congratulated Sean and with his permission used the scenario to test other processes while making a positive example of his actions.

Some might say that 'getting set' is an unnecessary step – that, after preparation, you can just go and do what you're preparing for. However, as we can see with the examples of baking a cake or testing an employee's reaction to something that doesn't go to plan, getting set means testing the process and also testing your staff – it is invaluable.

Pressure from others to execute quickly could make you feel the need to rush what you are doing. Resist this, if possible. Your success, and the success of what you do, lies in the planning and the delivery.

How can I take action?

Exercise 2

Rather than the usual checklist, create a quiz for your staff to ensure that they are set to go. For example, you could ask the following questions:

1. How many residents are involved in what you are planning?
2. Have all residents involved, and staff involved, been briefed on the action? And have any questions raised been addressed?
3. Is the equipment you are using fit for purpose?
4. Is the information provided for the action clear to everyone involved?
5. Do you have clear expectations for the action and have these been communicated?

The risk of staff being complacent is real – especially if they have been involved in the preparation. Creating a quiz keeps all staff involved in the process and truly engaged at every step, ensuring that things are ready to go.

GO

You're ready to go. You must see the importance of committing to your ideas and actions. Your ability to execute and get things done will be a key driver to your success, and to the success of what you want to achieve.

All the preparation and checking to see if you're set to go will mean nothing if you fail to launch.

The following story about the rock band U2 illustrates the importance of preparation, getting set and commitment to follow it through.

U2 started in Dublin. All the band members went to the same school. The band really struggled at the beginning. Adam Clayton, the bass player, suffered from depression which led to alcoholism. He later reflected that his drinking made him hard to put up with, but the band did anyway and took care of him.

It was 1987 in Tempe, Arizona, and U2 had just released their album *The Joshua Tree*. Their previous album was called *The Unforgettable Fire* and it included a song called 'Pride (In the Name of Love)'. The third verse in the song was about Martin Luther King and his tragic assassination.

U2 was playing gigs on 3 and 4 April, marking the anniversary of Martin Luther King's assassination (4 April 1968). It was their first show of the tour, and there was plenty of media attention.

On 3 April, the day of their first concert, they received a death threat – warning the band that if they played 'Pride' on 4 April, they would be shot. The band told the FBI, which said, 'With this short amount of time, there's no way we can protect you. He might be in the crowd with a handgun, he might be a sniper – there are just too many scenarios. You'll have to cancel the concert.'

U2 discussed it and decided to go ahead anyway. Towards the end of the concert, they played 'Pride'. As they came to the third verse, Bono – the lead singer – was terrified. He closed his eyes and sang the words relating to the assassination. He said that the whole time he was singing, he was expecting a bullet. He got to the end of the song with his eyes closed. When he opened them, he saw that the bass player, Adam Clayton, had been playing in front of him so no-one could shoot him. After the concert when they went back and debriefed, Adam said, 'You all protected me through my years. This was my way of protecting you.'[20]

Preparation and checking can only go so far. You must have the courage of your convictions to launch what you have planned. Get set, go and be true to your convictions like U2.

How can I take action?

Exercise 3

Follow through on the execution of your plan, and then reflect and evaluate what has occurred afterwards. Build some reflection time alone and with your team into your plan. This will be invaluable – not only in the process and outcome of your collective actions, but in building relationships with your staff.

CONCLUSION

Preparation is the key step in any delivery process. You must be sure that everything is in place and that all involved know exactly what is expected of them. These are vital steps to launching your work. However, all the preparation and checking will mean nothing if you fail to launch.

Make sure all your plans have the three steps of preparation – setting the scene to be in a great position – and then a step to launch. Build this into everything that you do.

What's coming up?

The next chapter summarises the key points we've discussed, bringing all the information and exercises together in one place.

9: The wrap up

In this chapter, you will find the key points and discoveries from chapters 1 to 8. This is a reference point for you – a place to visit in the future when you are presented with any challenge that occurs in your job of managing and leading in residential aged care. Later in this chapter, you will find a summary of all the exercises addressing the points I have discussed. Each exercise action has a direct link to the key points and discoveries.

My intention is for you to pick up this book and use it as a prompt. As you read the chapters, note what resonates with you and your work, highlight it and start building your own way of bringing about change in your workplace.

KEY POINTS AND DISCOVERIES FROM EACH CHAPTER

Chapter 1: Partnership

You must change your approach to delivering care and services to residents in your aged care home because the rules changed in July 2019. The first of the eight legislated changes specifically puts the resident at the centre of everything you do. It has never been articulated in this way before; it has been spelled out, so providers are in no doubt.

Because the rules have changed, your past performance and models cannot be relied upon to dictate how you operate your home. The changes are significant and require agility, innovation and good management to meet what is required. The changes require you to work in partnership with the resident – a big shift from doing *to*, to doing *with* – to design changes and tailor care and services, collectively and individually.

Do not underestimate the changes you will have to make to move from your current ways of working to designing care and services *with* the residents that suit the residents. To succeed at this, you must engage your staff in the changes to make the resident-staff working relationship a success.

Chapter 2: The shower list

The residents are your purpose – and so, in the home you manage, your goal is to improve the resident experience. It is your business to create a great resident experience.

Don't forget to create a great staff experience, too. Step into your role as manager, set out your expectations of staff and build their competence and confidence. Staff are your greatest asset but also your greatest challenge. Don't be too busy to get in the midst of what happens each day.

You are the leader. Don't allow unofficial leaders to 'breed' or take control in the absence of good leadership from you. Create a structure for your staff to work by and set expectations for them to follow so that they (and you) deliver on the outcomes and results you have determined are important.

Chapter 3: Communication

There is a difference between information and communication. Be crystal clear on the results and outcomes you seek every time you communicate with staff, residents and their families.

Change your communication style to suit the type of information you need to convey. Set expectations for staff through communication. Validate good communication by speaking to staff and asking for feedback.

Some meetings are necessary and unavoidable, but too many meetings will keep you from doing your job. Be selective about the meetings you create. The purpose of the meetings should guide you to stay on track.

Chapter 4: Culture

Understand the current culture at your home, determine the right attitude fit for your staff, and recruit to this to develop a positive culture. Hire the right people for the home you manage. Change the way you recruit so that you hire people for their cultural fit and attitude. Don't let skills, qualifications and experience alone guide your decisions to hire that person. There are new ways to recruit and onboard your staff.

Chapter 5: Risk

Learn how to become a 'risk ninja' – a master of risk – and know how and when to intervene and when not to do so. Risk is part of everyday operations.

There are three different types of risk – internal, desirable and external – and the approach taken should be matched with the level and category of risk.

Make sure you understand risk to a level that you can educate, mentor and coach your staff in the correct approach for each category.

Most people see risk as painful and something to avoid. As a manager and a leader, you must turn identifying and managing risk into a positive experience for your staff, residents and their families.

Determine what success looks like for risk management in the home you manage. Understand risk as one of the three categories and turn this into something practical for your staff to understand. Give examples to your staff so they are clear in their understanding.

Chapter 6: Authentic leadership

Being an authentic leader will give clarity to your understanding of who you are, what you stand for and what drives you. It enables you to become a better, more focused leader and to be someone who others wish to follow.

Not everyone relates or responds the same way to the same leadership style. Using your character, skill and style to suit the situation and the people you lead is a recipe for your success as a leader.

Match your leadership with the context of the situation. Focus on:

1. creating a vision
2. using data

3. using feedback effectively

4. creating engagement.

Learn how to share a little more of yourself each day.

Chapter 7: Know your residents

Use your assessment processes to get to know your residents. You will have myriad assessments – both clinical and non-clinical – that are completed routinely for each and every resident. Use them to their full capacity: take the information and use this with your staff to get to know your residents. Create a deeper understanding that will help refine outcomes.

Learn how to take feedback as a gift. Don't shy away from any feedback. Teach both your residents and your staff what they can do with feedback (compliments, complaints and suggestions). This will supercharge your business.

Define what great customer service is and deliver it. Understand what this means on every transaction: each time staff do something with or for a resident.

Chapter 8: Ready, set, go

Are you ready to take on the challenge of being a residential aged care manager? If you are in the job already, are you ready to change the way you operate in the job?

Get set. Being able to launch all the things you would like to achieve takes preparation and thought to plan.

How to take off: get your bag of tools and be ready to *go*.

EXERCISES AND TOOLS

Below are all the exercises that I outlined in each chapter, along with some extra tools you can use to put them into action. They are designed to help you with your job, develop your staff and turn the home you manage into one that is a delight to live and work in.

Chapter 1: Partnership

Exercise 1

Take a few minutes over the next week to simply sit in the lounge room, or a space where residents and staff usually interact, and observe what is going on. Consider the following questions:

- Are the residents active?
- Are the residents alert and engaged?
- Are the staff talking to the residents?

Afterwards, you may like to take some time to reflect on what you have seen. Try not to be confronted, but instead use the experience in a positive way. Here are some things you can do:

- go for a walk
- talk to a friend
- discuss your observations with a colleague
- write a list of action points.

Exercise 2

Spend some time getting to know who your residents are. The following questions are just a starting point:

- What has their life been like up until now?
- What has interested them?
- What has driven them?

Now, it's time to analyse your lifestyle agenda. Pull it apart with a group of residents and staff. Start with the important things:

- What are residents getting most enjoyment from?
- What time of the day suits residents to do activities?

While you're discussing and analysing, observe the interaction between staff and residents. Is it how you imagined it would be?

Exercise 3

Start the conversation with a few key staff about creating a workplace that is designed around what the residents really want. Choose a staff member from each of the three categories Merle talks about:

1. those who have passion, energy, a true resident focus and a love for their job
2. those who are indifferent
3. those who seem to actively dislike their job.

Begin by focusing on a mealtime or looking at the lifestyle agenda. Look at what's meaningful, and which residents – not just one or two – and their relatives you can bring into the conversation.

Ask residents if they would be happy to take part in a discussion where they will be invited to voice what they would really like to do each day, when they would like to eat, and how they would like their days and weeks to unfold.

You have now started your co-design piece of work. You might think, 'That's not enough to drive the serious change needed', but you have to start somewhere. If you have 100 residents, it's unwieldy to have the immediate input of 100 people – some of whom might be at an end-of-life stage, and some who may have severe cognitive decline. Bring a few in to begin, and then start widening that circle as you get some traction on the focus that you've decided on.

Let's say you decide to focus first on dining. You may see that 75 per cent of the people in your home eat in their rooms, because the staff say they can't manage everyone in the dining room. As you begin to make changes to this, and the more people come out of their rooms during mealtimes, the more people you involve.

Set a realistic timeline, say three months, and choose something that you can measure. Think about what success looks like in the focus that you have chosen. If it's about meals, and you've decided that you're going to change the dining experience around lunchtime, decide with your residents and staff how the meal service delivery, the conversation, the whole ambience should look in three months' time. Then you can start working out the steps backwards from there to where you are now. You have involved your residents and your staff, and now you've started your co-design piece to change the way you work – without adding extra staff.

Co-design tool

Step 1	Find out what matters most to residents.
Step 2	Ask both residents and staff who would be willing to be part of a group to design activities, schedules and so on around the things that matter most (co-design group).
Step 3	Gather experiences from residents and staff on the chosen field/subjects by either interview, survey or informal gatherings.
Step 4	Bring residents and staff together, explore findings and identify actions to improve the chosen filed/subject.

Step 5	Plan actions and deliverables with agreement from residents and staff.
Step 6	Put actions to test and then re-evaluate.

Chapter 2: The shower list

Exercise 1

Allocate a morning to work alongside your staff. Observe how the morning shift is structured and who does what.

Reflect on what you have seen. Some questions you may like to ponder include:

- Who did you put in charge of the morning shift – and who were your staff *actually* following?
- What routines appeared to be imbedded in the way the morning was run?
- Did the residents like being woken up at the time they were?
- Were any choices offered? How were these spoken about?
- How does the reality compare with what you thought you should have experienced?

Exercise 2

Create a daily huddle – a short meeting of five to ten minutes each morning – to concentrate the day's planning. Ask the following questions:

- Are we ready for today?
- Who needs our care in a particular way today?
- What are our priorities for today?
- What do we need to do to be ready for tomorrow?

The daily huddle must include all your key people – this shifts the attention off the multitude of lists, because you're focusing your staff on your residents and the here and now.

Then, as the day goes on, you can check in by asking:

- How are we doing?
- Are we going against the focus we've set today?
- How is Mrs or Mr So-and-So? We said they needed our special care in a certain way today.

This creates a language that is not present if you don't have a focus and set your expectations.

Exercise 3

Take the shower list, the linen list, the lunch list – in fact, any list that exists – and meet with your residents and staff to discuss it. Ask the following questions:

- What is important to the residents?
- What is important to staff?
- Who is the best person to lead your staff, shift by shift?

Ask the residents what bothers them most and what's most important to them about this list. Does it matter to them what time they are showered? Does it matter if they're not showered?

Your staff will see what the residents want. Then, ask your staff what's important to them. Sometimes staff members might feel they're not doing a good job because they're not washing somebody, rather than acknowledging that the resident doesn't want a shower.

After the meeting, help your staff. Lead by example shift by shift, and then start creating a structure and a culture around what the resident wants each day, each shift.

Chapter 3: Communication

Exercise 1

You can do this exercise section by section if the home you manage is large.

On a sheet of paper or whiteboard, map out what matters most to the resident you are working with. It may be that they were in the armed forces, a tradie, a seamstress, a nurse, a cook, an artist and so forth. Think about how their life's work and interests can be kept alive, if that is what they want and it matters to them.

Overlay this information with the resident's preference for daily items such as time of shower, meals, walks or afternoon naps.

Now, on your morning walk-around, ask staff:

· what they learned about the resident yesterday

· what they think others should know from what they learned.

Add this information to your resident map.

Exercise 2

Spend some time looking at how you can create clarity and set expectations through your meeting process, or perhaps your handover process. Let's take a look at your meetings.

Run effective meetings by categorising the information to be discussed into three sections:

1. For information

2. For discussion

3. For decision.

During the meeting, be vigilant about assessing the conversation and moving the discussion forward when needed:

- Is this useful to the discussion? Then proceed.
- Is this interesting but can be spoken of outside the meeting? Do not proceed, get back to the subject.

Clearly identify decisions and action steps decided during the meeting. Apply accountability to the decisions and action steps.

Produce action items to follow up. *And follow up.*

You or your staff may take some time to adjust to your new meeting system. Check in with everyone about how they're coping and try to solve problems as they arise.

Exercise 3

It's time to test how effective your communications really are. Here are some questions to consider when looking for feedback on the outcomes of your communications:

- Have I spoken to staff and let them know what is expected of them?
- Do staff come to work each shift and work by rote? (In other words, do staff turn up for their shift and carry out their work practices based on repetition?)
- Do staff assess each shift by resident need and change the order in which things are done based on their assessments?
- Have I enabled staff to join the dots between the residents' needs and wants to live the life they choose, and the tasks staff perceive to be important?

Have your staff received your message that residents' needs and wants should be the focus? Or are they coming to work with the attitude, 'This is my workplace and the residents just fit in'?

What do your staff see as important, and why do they think it is important? What can you do to better communicate what you, as their manager, know to be important?

Chapter 4: Culture

Exercise 1

It's time to take a deep dive into your hiring process, beginning with your job advertisement. What words can you add to your advertisement to tell people what your home is about and what you're looking for? How can you reflect, in your advertisement, the culture you are looking to create, so you can attract people who already have the right attitude? Think of the keywords you can include to shape the advertisement.

Next, look at your interview technique. I have seen so many examples of poor interviewing in aged care. One of the worst things you can do is run through a set of questions that are formulated and delivered as a list – no matter what the person answers, the next question is asked. You must probe and explore the candidate's responses, finding out as much about them as you can.

Ask your interviewees questions in a way that allows them to give you a picture of the type of person they are. Ask them to describe a situation ('Give me an example of a situation where...'): what they did; what the response was; and what they learned.

Exercise 2

Linking staff development to your organisational goals is a great way to help your staff understand their 'why'. Meet with your staff and be clear as you articulate what your home's focus is, and how each of them can play a part in achieving it. Provide context. When you want your staff to carry out something or think about their performance, give them real context around the daily situations in your home. You can then conduct expectation meetings with them.

Bring together small groups of staff who perform particular roles in your home and say, 'Let's go through the expectations of what is required of you each day and each month.' This may give clarity and smooth out any misalignments – for example, staff think their job is to do X and you think their job is to do Y. It's a good exercise to do and can be an eye opener for staff (and you!)

You might encourage your staff to use the planner below to track the progress of their goals, expectations and outcomes.

As you work through goals with your staff, be sure to incorporate failure points as markers. For example, consider a situation where staff think they know what the residents want and take the voice away from the residents themselves as a failure point. Use your planner as a road map; on the map, clearly mark 'Wrong way, turn back': this indicates a road that staff should not or could not go down. To reach the goal, you follow the road map. This helps people know whether or not they are on the right track.

Example goal planner

Goals	Expectations	Outcomes
Example Big Goal: All residents who are able are encouraged to help design a great dining experience for lunchtime.	All residents are given the opportunity to have input into what a great dining experience is. All staff are asked to have input into the dining experience. Staff experience the reality of eating at the dining table with residents as part of this process. Residents are given more input into the ambience, food and service experience for each meal.	Staff and residents give feedback and work together to create a great dining experience at lunchtime each day – progressing to all meals.

Take your Big Goal and work out your short-term goals on the way to achieving your Big Goal. What do you have to achieve in this quarter to move closer to your Big Goal?

Remind yourself of them here and write them in the present tense.

Month 1 Goals/Outcomes	Month 2 Goals/Outcomes	Month 3 Goals/Outcomes

Exercise 3

In exercise 2 you set expectations and goals with your staff. Now is the time for you to support your goals to meet the goals you have set:

- Allow staff time to do the things set out without interference.
- Set reasonable timeframes to check in with your staff members. Perhaps say that you would like this outcome within a week or a month and set a check-in time. Say, 'How about I check in next Wednesday to see how you are going?'
- Don't micromanage the staff or the situation; this won't give you the results you hope for.

Chapter 5: Risk

Exercise 1

Take a situation such as a resident with dementia who, despite all controls, wanders out of the home.

Divide the staff members that you've gathered together into three groups, and give each group one of the following questions:

- What is the resident's diagnosis and associated behaviours?
- What controls do you have in place?
- What will disrupt this, and how?

You're the controller of what's going on and you can alter each aspect of the game to enable your staff to think rather than just follow instructions. This is called 'war gaming' – deconstructing and then constructing a situation. It allows your staff to go back and say, 'Okay. We know Janice has dementia. We know she's dressed in this way, and we have all the doors locked. Does every staff member know about this? Does every staff member understand the implications? Do all the families that come in understand this?'

We then see that there is a risk that a visitor will open the door for a resident who says, 'Can you let me out, please?' This is a risk. It's an internal risk because it's a preventable risk, and you can work on this with your staff to manage it.

Alternatively, you can use a desirable risk such as a resident wanting to go swimming with dolphins, or shopping using his or her mobility scooter in the local town without any assistance. There are so many examples of risk you could think of that are desirable and you could potentially accommodate.

Exercise 2

Make good use of the risk-management software you have in your organisation. Make sure you understand the three categories of risk for your home and the industry:

· internal

· desirable

· external.

Use a compliance approach where needed, such as when dealing with the internal or preventable risks.

There are lots of different risks, so perhaps you could map each risk out with your staff using a traffic light approach. Each risk could be divided into categories: what's definitely not going to happen, what's possible to take action on, and what's great. This approach can provide staff with examples and give them ideas of where to go with risks in each category.

Exercise 3

It's time to focus on the dignity of risk. Have a brainstorming session with your staff and residents and collect all their ideas for potential desirable risks: things residents would like to do and staff are capable of enabling. Encourage the residents to express their heart's desires rather than what they think would be allowed. Collectively, look at the risks with the residents and start mapping things out so that you have a live mind-map of the risks that are possible and where you're going to go with them.

Plan to discuss this with new residents (and their families) as they enter your home, too. You could do this activity once a month with all residents, and also each time a new resident comes to live at the home.

Often staff don't think they have permission to change how things happen in the home – perhaps they think risk is a formula that they have to follow, and that they must do what the regulator is instructing them to do. Some residents feel the home is an institution, as we heard Merle describe in chapter 1. This exercise challenges those ideas, positioning your home as a place where people can end their days in the most normal, happy way.

Chapter 6: Authentic leadership

Exercise 1

Draw up a table with three columns. In the first column, list some examples of how you think an authentic leader behaves. In the second column, list some examples of how you think a traditional leader behaves. In the third column, list how you perceive your leadership style. The following table is an example with the first two columns to get you started.

Leadership style audit

Authentic leader	Traditional leader	My leadership style
Lead with purpose	Lead with goals	
Lead with values and principles	Lead with someone else's agenda	
Lead by example and encouraging others	Lead by exerting power and control	

When you complete column three, can you see the similarities and differences with the other two columns? What can you draw from the authentic leadership column that is different to your current leadership style?

Exercise 2a

Write a few words about your leadership purpose, then ask others about what they see is your leadership purpose. You could ask: if you were to disappear from your current job and someone of equal standing (in terms of skills and knowledge) took your place, what would people miss about you? The answer to the question should bring clarity to your leadership purpose.

Think back to a time when you have been faced with a situation that has changed your thinking and therefore the way you live, a time when you have put yourself in an uncomfortable situation to grow and stretch your capabilities. Put your thoughts and then your words to these three questions:

- Who am I?

- What do I stand for?
- What drives me?

Now that you have completed this exercise, you can go back to it time and time again, refining your thoughts and crafting your words to truly reflect who you are.

Exercise 2b

This activity is called snakes and ladders.[21] Here's how to play:

- Take an A4 piece of paper.
- Draw a curvy line from the bottom left corner to the top right corner.
- At the bottom left corner, map out your journey or a part of your life such as your work.
- Work from bottom to top.
- With a green pen, mark the situations or things that have enabled your journey (the ladders) – for example, gaining a qualification, getting a job you wanted or buying a car.
- With a red pen, mark the situations or things that have blocked your journey (the snakes) – for example, missing out on a job you wanted, taking a road you didn't want to travel or taking a step backwards rather than forwards.
- Use this exercise as your own road map, and learn from the snakes and ladders. What are they? What occurred? What did you learn and apply from them? Be creative.

Exercise 3

I call this exercise Desert Island. Here's how it works:

- Ask each of your team members to select five music tracks and three books that they would take with them to a desert island.

- When the boat arrives to take them to the island, advise your team members that they must only take a maximum of three musical tracks and three books between them as weight restrictions apply.
- Ask the team to decide which tracks and books should be taken. An agreement must be made (collectively).

The objective of this exercise is for the team to understand that finite resources can still lead to a good outcome. You might start out with plentiful staff or resources that, for one reason or another, have to be cut back. You still have to deliver an outcome: in your case, a great resident experience.

Chapter 7: Know your residents

Exercise 1

Try this exercise:

- Each time the resident of the day process occurs, turn it into a teaching opportunity. Use the tool to gather information and teach from it.
- After the process has been completed, and the information gathered and documented, for the following 24 hours ask your staff questions such as, 'What did we learn about Mr Singh or Mrs Potter that we didn't know before?'
- Repeat this on each shift until all the shifts have had the same conversations during the month and reflect on the differences this has made to staff understanding and resident outcomes.

Changing routines for staff often has a downside. 'We don't like change' is a war cry in residential aged care. But give staff permission to use this tool as a way to enhance the handover process and see what they come up with from this exercise. Don't be prescriptive. They will say that the handover has to be short and sharp, and routinely staff are not given much time to hand over between shifts. If the information they're providing isn't relevant, ask them to look at a different way of doing things.

Exercise 2a

Take the feedback challenge. Gather together some of your key staff, or staff you would like to encourage to engage further with feedback.

Ask them to:

- Review your home's website. Write down what is great about the site, and what could be presented better.
- Roleplay the information a new resident and their family are given before and on arrival to the home. Discuss any improvements that could be made.
- Workshop the 'welcome to the home' process and its pros and cons.
- Observe a new resident's journey into the home, and what happens within their first four weeks. Consider that experience from the resident's perspective and discuss positives and negatives.

Now ask your staff what works well and what can be improved. You can repeat this exercise with a number of staff or groups of staff.

Exercise 2b

Consider your customer interactions. Script greetings and daily interactions for:

- answering the phone
- entering a resident's room

- addressing a resident and finding out if their title or first name is acceptable for them
- receiving feedback, responding to it and the next steps.

Changing the way staff use their words can be tricky, especially if English isn't their first language. However, it's important to set expectations early on about what great customer service is and give your staff scripts to learn about tone and consistency.

Exercise 3

Engaging staff through exercises to show them how to deliver great customer service is beneficial to your residents, staff and the business as a whole.

Using stories is a great way to engage your staff in customer service. For example, think of a time when you have received both good and bad customer service, and how that made you feel. You can ask staff to participate in this exercise as everyone has a story.

Next, conduct an exercise with staff where you draw four boxes.

In the top left-hand box, write: 'What does great customer service mean in the home that you work in?' In the top right-hand box, write: 'What does great customer service mean to me?'

In the bottom left-hand box, brainstorm everything concerning customer service you and your staff can think of.

In the bottom right-hand box, identify what each benefit means to the resident and what it means to staff. Then, prioritise the top five benefits to you and to the home you work in:

- List the benefits.
- Identify all potential objections/barriers.
- Find ways to overcome the objections/barriers to create the top five benefits.

When identifying the objections or barriers to providing first-class customer service, give staff permission to think about what they would like to receive. Create the environment to assist your staff. You cannot create the change in isolation – you need your staff to be part of this.

Chapter 8: Ready, set, go

Exercise 1

Getting ready takes thought and planning. Sometimes you need another person's opinion to counterbalance your own.

Ask someone who is successful in change management to give you their take on how you manage your people and get things done. Their insights may prove helpful to you. Ask them how they go about change and see how they manage the things you are hopeful of achieving.

Now, write down what you have taken from the conversation and decide whether it can be of use to your preparations. You can repeat this exercise as many times as is helpful for you. Everyone has a slightly different approach, and by talking through your issues with someone more experienced you may get some really good insights into your own behaviours, as well as picking up some tried-and-true methods from others.

Exercise 2

Rather than the usual checklist, create a quiz for your staff to ensure that they are set to go. For example, you could ask the following questions:

1. How many residents are involved in what you are planning?
2. Have all residents involved, and staff involved, been briefed on the action? And have any questions raised been addressed?

3. Is the equipment you are using fit for purpose?

4. Is the information provided for the action clear to everyone involved?

5. Do you have clear expectations for the action and have these been communicated?

The risk of staff being complacent is real – especially if they have been involved in the preparation. Creating a quiz keeps all staff involved in the process and truly engaged at every step, ensuring that things are ready to go.

Exercise 3

Follow through on the execution of your plan, and then reflect and evaluate what has occurred afterwards. Build some reflection time alone and with your team into your plan. This will be invaluable – not only in the process and outcome of your collective actions, but in building relationships with your staff.

CONCLUSION

Change can be hard to initiate and it's even harder sometimes to keep up momentum. Use these exercises to break down misconceptions. This book is intended as a reference to your daily life in both leading and managing in aged care.

In his 2017 article, 'Execution is a people problem not a strategy problem', Peter Bregman said an organisation's biggest problem is not strategic thinking, it is strategic acting.[22] You can have all the best-laid strategies and plans known to the human race, however if you can't engage and inspire your people these are not worth the effort or paper they are written on.

Final thoughts

Leading and managing in residential aged care is not for the faint-hearted; but when you know how, working with the elderly and the people who care for them can be so rewarding. Make the home you manage a great place to live and work. Take control and set the scene each day around how the day will pan out. Engage people – residents, their relatives and your staff. Use games and exercises to bring fun to learning. Even the most ardent opposer will either fall in, or leave.

My goal in writing this book is to help you have greater clarity and focus on how to direct your energy and manage your time more effectively. I hope I've inspired you to lead from both your head and your heart. You can't be all things to all people, but you can be the best in the home you manage – and you can start by changing things for the better, to be in good shape for everything to come. The Royal Commission into Aged Care Quality and Safety focused on the industry's current systems and how they are regulated. Now that you have read this book and undertaken the exercises, you will have an idea about how to think and work differently to reshape what you have now. You are the manager. Step into your power and make things happen. Craft something that is attractive and works.

Always keep the residents at the centre of your day and what you do. Make this a priority for your staff. Create safety, quality and fun in everything you do.

Wherever you look, information seems to be prolific in residential aged care. The implementation of appropriate actions has become an obstacle for effective change. Don't give in to detractors. There are plenty of people that say, 'I've tried that. That won't work. No, you can't do that.' Understand the 'why' behind what you're doing. Be passionate, be a resident advocate and stand your ground.

Imagine living in a residential home. What would matter most to you? How are you different from the people who are living in the home you manage? Free your thoughts from constriction and be yourself when designing great care and services with the residents who live in the home you manage. Don't do this in isolation.

I hope that you will be energised to manage a home that is happy and allows the things that matter most to people to be realised – and that you find joy in the work that you do.

CONNECT WITH ME

Since you have read this book, I know you are a leader who is committed to becoming the best you can be. If you've lost a little of the joy your career once held, a lot of your work-life balance and much of your vision for world-class leadership, perhaps I can help. I work with leaders in aged care to achieve their highest potential, boost confidence, advance their careers, develop themselves, sustain change and embrace new opportunities. I'd love for you to become part of the growing community of leaders who are actively working to change our sector for the better. You can contact me at www.theleadershipplace.com.au.

About the author

Allison Patchett is an expert in leading and managing people. She has spent her whole career working with people, building teams to operate successfully; she has coached and mentored numerous senior executives and middle managers in large and small organisations. Over the past 40 years she has learned a lot about people – particularly those working in hospital care, community care and residential aged care. It was her work in residential aged care where she really grasped the meaning of what matters most to older people; how short life is (even to a person in their 80s) and how precious life is. The challenges of meeting resident choice and needs while also building and developing staff in a highly regulated environment have brought about her own growth in working with people and assisting people to grow.

Allison believes that reading people is a skill – the rhythm of thoughts, actions and body language all speak the subtext of any spoken language. The art in her coaching is in the ability to read this and focus on what to draw out, what to build and what is positive.

She is the founder and managing director of The Leadership Place – a portfolio consultancy offering individual and organisational coaching and mentoring, middle management training in aged care, risk management in health, and a nurse adviser and administrator in residential aged care. Allison is also a board director on a public health board and chair of the quality and clinical risk board committee.

When Allison isn't working, she is happily ensconced in her life in country Victoria where she lives with her husband on acreage. At present they have a dog, cat and goats and are visited daily by large mobs of kangaroos, often accompanied by emus and koalas. Her sons visit often and have developed a love of the peace and tranquillity country life has to offer. Originally from England, Allison feels the south-western Victorian coastline and countryside remind her of Britain – this makes her feel very much at home nestled within its landscape.

Acknowledgements

The year 2020 was a hell of a year for everyone. Some benefited; most did not. The world has changed, as have we. It was during this year that my work took on a new focus: on helping middle managers in aged care, who needed assistance in a time of crisis. This also gave birth to the ideas in this book.

None of this would have been possible without the support of those around me, and those who have helped me.

Huge thanks to Kath Walters, book coach extraordinaire, without whom this book would still be in my thoughts. Also to Brooke Lyons, who is the most empathetic book editor you could wish for – she is an exceptional wordsmith.

To my family, parents, grandparents, husband and sons who have all shaped me and inspired me to make the most of what I can offer to other people. Each in their own way, they have shown me how courage, resilience and being thankful for even the small things makes for a brighter day.

And of course to the many people I have had the honour of working with over the years: each interaction has given me experiences from which to draw. Thank you.

References

1. Commonwealth of Australia 2021, 'COVID-19 outbreaks in Australian residential aged care facilities – 9 April 2021', health. gov.au/resources/publications/covid-19-outbreaks-in-australian-residential-aged-care-facilities-9-april-2021.

2. Commonwealth of Australia 2021, 'Statement of Barbara Elizabeth Spriggs', Royal Commission into Aged Care Quality and Safety, agedcare.royalcommission.gov.au/system/files/2020-06/ WIT.0025.0001.0001.pdf.

3. Cousins, S 2020, 'Experts criticise Australia's aged care failings over COVID-19', Lancet, ncbi.nlm.nih.gov/pmc/articles/ PMC7581404.

4. International Fire Service Training Association 1988, *Fire Department Company Officer*, 3rd Edition.

5. Gulati, R 2018, 'Structure that's not stifling', *Harvard Business Review*, hbr.org/2018/05/structure-thats-not-stifling.

6. ibid.

7. Commonwealth of Australia 2019, 'Interim Report', Royal Commission into Aged Care Quality and Safety, agedcare. royalcommission.gov.au/publications/interim-report.

8. Blanchard, K & Johnson, S 1982, *The One Minute Manager*, William Morrow & Co.

9. Cousins, S 2020, op. cit.

10. McKinsey & Company 2015, 'Building capabilities for performance', mckinsey.com/business-functions/organization/our-insights/building-capabilities-for-performance.

11. ABC Television 2017, *Old People's Home for 4 Year Olds* [television program], ABC Television, Sydney.

12. Frei, FX & Morriss, A 2020, 'Begin with trust', *Harvard Business Review*, hbr.org/2020/05/begin-with-trust.

13. Commonwealth of Australia 2020, *Aged care and COVID-19: a special report*, Royal Commission into Aged Care Quality and Safety, agedcare.royalcommission.gov.au/sites/default/files/2020-12/aged-care-and-covid-19-a-special-report.pdf.

14. ibid.

15. George, B 2015, *Discover Your True North*, Jossey-Bass.

16. This activity is reproduced with permission. Craig, N, George, B & Snook, S 2015, *Discover Your True North Fieldbook*, Wiley.

17. Anecdote International 2020, '082 – Corporate Storytelling—Leadership communication with Hannah Davies', anecdote.com/2020/11/082-corporate-storytelling-leadership-communication-with-hannah-davies.

18. Harter, J 2020, 'Historic drop in employee engagement follows record rise', Gallup, gallup.com/workplace/313313/historic-drop-employee-engagement-follows-record-rise.aspx.

19. Anecdote International 2019, '046 – Work the plan and work with the people', anecdote.com/2019/08/work-plan-people-46.

20. Anecdote International 2018, '024 – U2 can protect your tribe', anecdote.com/2018/06/u2-can-protect-tribe-episode-24.

21. This activity is reproduced with permission. Craig, N, George, B & Snook, S 2015, op. cit.

22. Bregman, P 2017, 'Execution is a people problem, not a strategy problem', *Harvard Business Review*, hbr.org/2017/01/execution-is-a-people-problem-not-a-strategy-problem.